It's All the Same

Geometry and Measurement

BRITANNICA
Mathematics in Context

TEACHER'S GUIDE

HOLT, RINEHART AND WINSTON

Mathematics in Context is a comprehensive curriculum for the middle grades. It was developed in 1991 through 1997 in collaboration with the Wisconsin Center for Education Research, School of Education, University of Wisconsin-Madison and the Freudenthal Institute at the University of Utrecht, The Netherlands, with the support of the National Science Foundation Grant No. 9054928.

The revision of the curriculum was carried out in 2003 through 2005, with the support of the National Science Foundation Grant No. ESI 0137414.

National Science Foundation

Opinions expressed are those of the authors
and not necessarily those of the Foundation.

Roodhardt, A.; Abels, M.; de Lange, J.; Dekker, T.; Clarke, B.; Clarke, D. M.; Spence, M. S.; Shew, J. A.; Brinker, L. J.; and Pligge, M. A. (2006). *It's all the same.* In Wisconsin Center for Education Research & Freudenthal Institute (Eds.), *Mathematics in context.* Chicago: Encyclopædia Britannica, Inc.

The Teacher's Guide for this unit was prepared by David C. Webb, Elaine McGrath, Els Feijs, Jan de Lange, and Truus Dekker.

ISBN 0-03-039828-2

3 4 5 6   073   09 08 07

The *Mathematics in Context* Development Team

Development 1991–1997

The initial version of *Triangles and Patchwork* was developed by Anton Roodhardt and Mieke Abels. It was adapted for use in American schools by Barbara Clarke, Doug M. Clarke, Mary C. Spence, Julia A. Shew, and Laura J. Brinker.

Wisconsin Center for Education

Research Staff

Thomas A. Romberg
Director

Joan Daniels Pedro
Assistant to the Director

Gail Burrill
Coordinator

Margaret R. Meyer
Coordinator

Project Staff

Jonathan Brendefur
Laura Brinker
James Browne
Jack Burrill
Rose Byrd
Peter Christiansen
Barbara Clarke
Doug Clarke
Beth R. Cole
Fae Dremock
Mary Ann Fix

Sherian Foster
James A, Middleton
Jasmina Milinkovic
Margaret A. Pligge
Mary C. Shafer
Julia A. Shew
Aaron N. Simon
Marvin Smith
Stephanie Z. Smith
Mary S. Spence

Freudenthal Institute Staff

Jan de Lange
Director

Els Feijs
Coordinator

Martin van Reeuwijk
Coordinator

Mieke Abels
Nina Boswinkel
Frans van Galen
Koeno Gravemeijer
Marja van den Heuvel-Panhuizen
Jan Auke de Jong
Vincent Jonker
Ronald Keijzer
Martin Kindt

Jansie Niehaus
Nanda Querelle
Anton Roodhardt
Leen Streefland
Adri Treffers
Monica Wijers
Astrid de Wild

Revision 2003–2005

The revised version of *It's All the Same* was developed by Jan de Lange, Mieke Abels, and Truus Dekker. It was adapted for use in American schools by Margaret A. Pligge.

Wisconsin Center for Education

Research Staff

Thomas A. Romberg
Director

David C. Webb
Coordinator

Gail Burrill
Editorial Coordinator

Margaret A. Pligge
Editorial Coordinator

Project Staff

Sarah Ailts
Beth R. Cole
Erin Hazlett
Teri Hedges
Karen Hoiberg
Carrie Johnson
Jean Krusi
Elaine McGrath

Margaret R. Meyer
Anne Park
Bryna Rappaport
Kathleen A. Steele
Ana C. Stephens
Candace Ulmer
Jill Vettrus

Freudenthal Institute Staff

Jan de Lange
Director

Truus Dekker
Coordinator

Mieke Abels
Content Coordinator

Monica Wijers
Content Coordinator

Arthur Bakker
Peter Boon
Els Feijs
Dédé de Haan
Martin Kindt

Nathalie Kuijpers
Huub Nilwik
Sonia Palha
Nanda Querelle
Martin van Reeuwijk

Cover photo credits: (left) © Corbis; (middle, right) © Getty Images

Illustrations
x Map from the Road Atlas © 1994 by Rand McNally;
(right) © Encyclopædia Britannica, Inc.; **xii** (bottom), **xiii** (top right) Holly Cooper-Olds; **xviii** (left) Christine McCabe/©Encyclopædia Britannica, Inc.; **14** (top) Rich Stergulz; (middle) Christine McCabe/© Encyclopædia Britannica, Inc.; **15** Christine McCabe/© Encyclopædia Britannica, Inc.; **33, 39, 43** Rich Stergulz; **44, 48** Christine McCabe/© Encyclopædia Britannica, Inc.

Photographs
x Historic Urban Plans, Inc.; **xiii** Courtesy of Michigan State University Museum; **xvii** © Corbis; **11** © Comstock, Inc.; **27** Sam Dudgeon/HRW Photo; **29** Andy Christiansen/HRW; **31** HRW Art; **36** Andy Christiansen/HRW; **40** Victoria Smith/HRW; **44** (top left, right, bottom left) PhotoDisc/Getty Images; (bottom right) © Corbis; **54** © PhotoDisc/Getty Images

Contents

Dear Teacher,

Welcome! *Mathematics in Context* is designed to reflect the National Council of Teachers of Mathematics *Principles and Standards for School Mathematics* and the results of decades of classroom-based education research. *Mathematics in Context* was designed according to principles of Realistic Mathematics Education, a Dutch approach to mathematics teaching and learning where mathematical content is grounded in a variety of realistic contexts to promote student engagement and understanding of mathematics. The term *realistic* is meant to convey that the contexts and mathematics can be made "real in your mind." Rather than relying on you to explain and demonstrate generalized definitions, rules, or algorithms, students investigate questions directly related to a particular context and develop mathematical understanding and meaning from that context.

The curriculum encompasses nine units per grade level. This unit is designed to be the sixth unit in the Geometry and Measurement strand, but it also lends itself to independent use—to introduce students to identifying congruent and similar figures, using ratios and multipliers, proving that triangles are similar, and using the properties of similar triangles to solve problems.

In addition to the Teacher's Guide and Student Books, *Mathematics in Context* offers the following components that will inform and support your teaching

- *Teacher Implementation Guide,* which provides an overview of the complete system and resources for program implementation;

- *Number Tools* and *Algebra Tools,* which are black-line master resources that serve as intervention sheets or practice pages to support the development of basic skills and extend student understanding of concepts developed in number and algebra units; and

- *Mathematics in Context Online,* which is a rich, balanced resource for teachers, students, and parents looking for additional information, activities, tools, and support to further students' mathematical understanding and achievements.

Thank you for choosing *Mathematics in Context*. We wish you success and inspiration!

Sincerely,

The Mathematics in Context Development Team

It's All the Same and the NCTM Principles and Standards for School Mathematics for Grades 6–8

The process standards of Problem Solving, Reasoning and Proof, Communication, Connections, and Representation are addressed across all *Mathematics in Context* units.

In addition, this unit specifically addresses the following PSSM content standards and expectations:

Geometry

In grades 6–8, all students should:

- precisely describe, classify, and understand relationships among types of two- and three-dimensional objects using their defining properties;
- understand relationships among the angles, side lengths, perimeters, areas, and volumes of similar objects;
- create and critique inductive and deductive arguments concerning geometric ideas and relationships, such as congruence, similarity, and the Pythagorean relationship;
- use coordinate geometry to represent and examine the properties of geometric shapes;
- use coordinate geometry to examine special geometric shapes, such as regular polygons or those with pairs of parallel and perpendicular sides;
- describe sizes, positions, and orientations of shapes under informal transformations, such as flips, turns, slides, and scaling;
- examine the congruence, similarity, and line or rotational symmetry of objects using transformations;
- draw geometric objects with specified properties, such as side lengths or angle measures;
- use geometric models to represent and explain numerical and algebraic relationships; and
- recognize and apply geometric ideas and relationships in areas outside the mathematics classroom.

Measurement

In grades 6–8 all students should:

- understand, select, and use units of appropriate size and type to measure angles, perimeter, area, surface area, and volume;
- select and apply techniques and tools to accurately find length, area, volume, and angle measures to appropriate levels of precision; and
- solve problems involving scale factors, using ratio and proportion.

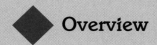
Math in the Unit

Prior Knowledge

This unit assumes students:

- can use ratios and ratio tables to solve numerical problems;

- know the basic properties of triangles; for example, the angle measurements add up to 180°;

- know the properties of parallel lines;

- can use the Pythagorean theorem to calculate the lengths of sides in a right triangle;

- know the basic properties of quadrilaterals: rectangle, parallelogram, and rhombus;

- recognize types of angles: acute angle (<90°), obtuse angle (>90°), right angle (90°); and

- recognize types of triangles: equilateral (all sides equal, all angles 60°), isosceles (two equal sides, two equal angles).

The unit *It's All the Same* builds upon the concepts introduced in the unit *Triangles and Beyond*. Students investigate the properties of similar triangles at a formal level, and more formal mathematical language is introduced and used throughout this unit. *Tessellation*, or covering of a surface with congruent figures and cutting the tessellation along parallel lines, is an activity used to introduce the concepts of congruent and similar triangles.

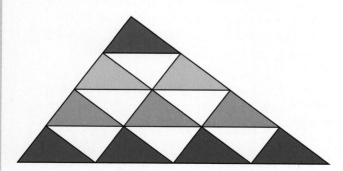

Students analyze the relationships in resulting tessellations by asking such questions as, *How many triangles in total would tessellate the large triangle if there were five rows? Ten rows? △ rows?* The number of small, dark triangles along each side of a larger triangle serves as an introduction of the *enlargement factor*. The *multiplication factor* encompasses either an enlargement or a reduction: if the multiplication factor is a number between 0 and 1, the dimensions of the original object are reduced; if the multiplication factor is larger than 1, the dimensions are enlarged.

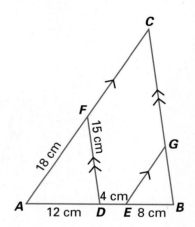

Students identify and construct similar triangles to calculate measurements, using the multiplication factor, a ratio table, or tessellations. They use different strategies to organize measurements of similar triangles and formally investigate corresponding angles and sides. For example, in the overlapping triangles figure, they find all the sets of similar triangles, identify corresponding sides and angles, and calculate the lengths of line segments *FC*, *BG*, *CG*, and *EG*.

Students also apply their knowledge when solving realistic problems, such as calculating the height of a bridge above a river and the width of an open stepladder, or estimating the height of a tree.

Students make generalizations about the angles formed when parallel lines are intersected by a transversal; for example, alternate interior angles and corresponding angles are congruent. In the last section of the unit, the content of the previous sections, as well as from former units, is formalized in the mathematical context of coordinate geometry. Students review the concept that parallel lines in a coordinate system have the same slope, and that perpendicular lines have slopes that are each other's negative reciprocal, for example, −2 and $\frac{1}{2}$. The slopes of lines are, likewise, used to prove whether intersecting lines are perpendicular. Students use the Pythagorean theorem to calculate the lengths of line segments to prove whether or not a quadrilateral is a rhombus and whether the diagonals for a rectangle have the same length.

The Pythagorean theorem is also used to calculate the distance between two separate points on a grid. When students have finished the unit, they:

- understand and use the concept of congruent and similar figures;
  - Students begin with an informal definition of congruency: *Congruent figures are exact copies.* This is formalized later as: *Two figures are congruent if they have the same size and the same shape.*
  - They use a multiplication factor to find unknown lengths of similar figures.
  - Students develop different strategies to calculate unknown lengths of similar triangles.
  - They express the multiplication factor both as a ratio and a percent.
  - They use formal notations such as *ABCD ~ DEFG* and learn, for example, that the same angle in triangle *DAB* can be written as either ∠A or ∠DAB.
  - Students know that if triangles are similar, their corresponding sides have the same ratio, and their corresponding angles are equal, and vice versa.
- understand the relationship between angles and parallel lines;
  - Students use tessellations to explore intersecting families of parallel lines and find corresponding and alternate interior angles are equal in size, and vice versa.
- use the properties of similar triangles and parallel lines to solve problems; and
  - They use these properties to prove, for example, whether a quadrilateral is a rectangle, rhombus, or parallelogram.
- know and use formal properties of straight lines in a coordinate system.
  - Students use the Pythagorean theorem to calculate the length of line segments and the distance between two separate points in a coordinate system.
  - Students use the rule that the sum of the angle measurements in a triangle is 180°.

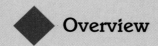

Geometry and Measurement Strand: An Overview

In the MiC units, measurement concepts and skills are not treated as a separate strand. Many measurement topics are closely related to what students learn in geometry. The geometry and measurement units contain topics such as similarity, congruency, perimeter, area, and volume. The identification of and application with a variety of shapes, both two-dimensional and three dimensional, is also addressed.

The developmental principles behind geometry in *Mathematics in Context* are drawn from Hans Freudenthal's idea of "grasping space." Throughout the strand, ideas of geometry and measurement are explored. Geometry includes movement and space—not just the study of shapes. The major goals for this strand are to develop students' ability to describe what is seen from different perspectives and to use principles of orientation and navigation to find their way from one place to another.

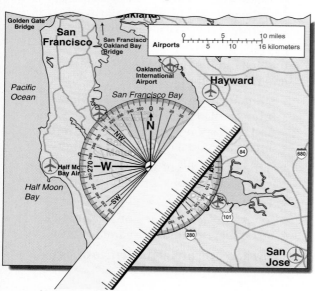

The emphasis on spatial sense is related to how most people actually use geometry. The development of students' spatial sense allows them to solve problems in the real world, such as identifying a car's blind spots, figuring out how much material to buy for a project, deciding whether a roof or ramp is too steep, and finding the height or length of something that cannot be measured directly, such as a tree or a building.

Mathematical content

In *Mathematics in Context*, geometry is firmly anchored in the physical world. The problem contexts involve space and action, and students represent these physical relationships mathematically.

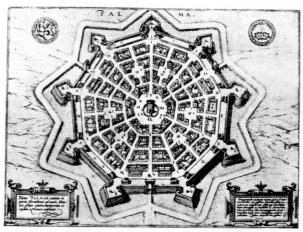

Throughout the curriculum, students discover relationships between shapes and develop the ability to explain and use geometry in the real world. By the end of the curriculum, students work more formally with such geometric concepts as parallelism, congruence, and similarity, and use traditional methods of notation as well.

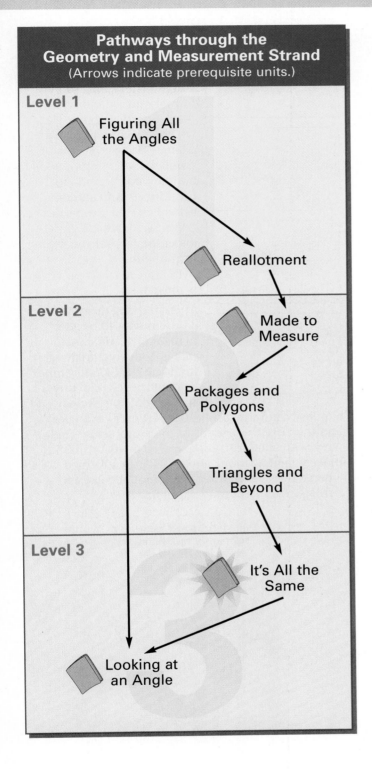

**Pathways through the
Geometry and Measurement Strand**
(Arrows indicate prerequisite units.)

Level 1

Figuring All
the Angles

Reallotment

Level 2

Made to
Measure

Packages and
Polygons

Triangles and
Beyond

Level 3

It's All the
Same

Looking at
an Angle

Organization of the Geometry and Measurement Strand

Visualization and representation is a pervasive theme in the Geometry strand and is developed in all of the Geometry and Measurement strand units. The units are organized into two substrands: Orientation and Navigation, and Shape and Construction. The development of measurement skills and concepts overlaps these two substrands and is also integrated throughout other *Mathematics in Context* units in Number, Algebra, and Data Analysis.

Orientation and Navigation

The Orientation and Navigation substrand is introduced in *Figuring All the Angles*, in which students are introduced to the cardinal, or compass, directions and deal with the problems that arise when people in different positions describe a location with directions. Students use maps and compass headings to identify the positions of airplanes. They look at angles as turns, or changes in direction, as well as the track made by a sled in the snow. They discern different types of angles and learn formal notations and terms: vertex, $\angle A$, and so on. The rule for the sum of the angles in a triangle is informally introduced. To find angle measurements students use instruments such as a protractor and compass card.

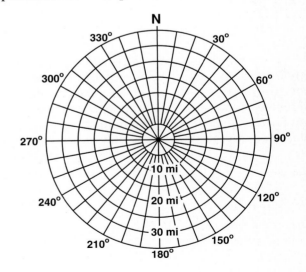

Overview

In *Looking at an Angle*, the last unit in the Geometry strand, the tangent ratio is informally introduced. The steepness of a vision line, the sun's rays, a ladder, and the flight path of a hang glider can all be modeled by a right triangle. Considering the glide ratio of hang gliders leads to formalization of the tangent ratio. Two other ratios between the sides of a right triangle are introduced, the sine and the cosine. This leads to formalization of the use of the Pythagorean theorem and its converse.

Shape and Construction

Reallotment is the first unit in the Shape and Construction substrand. Students measure and calculate the perimeters and areas of quadrilaterals, circles, triangles, and irregular polygons. Students learn and use relations between units of measurement within the Customary system and the Metric System.

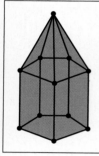

Does Euler's formula work for a five-sided tower? Explain your answer

Solids are introduced in *Packages and Polygons*. Students compare polyhedra with their respective nets, use bar models to understand the concept of rigidity, and use Euler's formula to formally investigate the relationships among the numbers of faces, vertices, and edges of polyhedra.

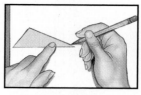
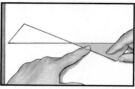
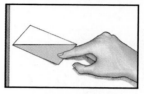
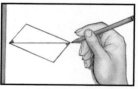

In *Triangles and Beyond*, students develop a more formal understanding of the properties of triangles, which they use to construct triangles. The concepts of parallel lines, congruence, and transformation are introduced, and students investigate the properties of parallel lines and parallelograms. A preformal introduction to the Pythagorean theorem is presented.

After studying this unit, students should be able to recognize and classify triangles and quadrilaterals. In the unit *It's All the Same*, students develop an understanding of congruency, similarity, and the properties of similar triangles and then use these ideas to solve problems. Their work with similarity and parallelism leads them to make generalizations about the angles formed when a transversal intersects parallel lines, and the Pythagorean theorem is formalized.

If a triangle has a right angle, then the square on the longest side has the same area as the other two combined.

Measurement

The concept of a measurement system, standard-ized units, and their application overlaps the sub-strands of Orientation and Navigation, and Shape and Construction. Furthermore, the development and application of measurement skills is integrated throughout units in the Number, Algebra, and Data Analysis strands, through topics such as use of ratio and proportion, finding and applying scale factors, and solving problems involving rates (for instance, distance-velocity-time relationships).

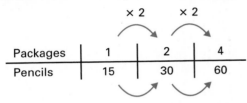

		× 2	× 2
Packages	1	2	4
Pencils	15	30	60

In *Mathematics in Context*, the Metric System is used not only as a measurement system, but also as a model to promote understanding of decimal numbers.

The unit *Made to Measure* is a thematic measure-ment unit where students work with standard and non-standard units to understand the systems and processes of measurement. They begin by studying historic units of measure such as foot, pace, and fathom (the length of outstretched arms). Students use their own measurements in activities about length, area, volume, and angle and then examine why standardized units are necessary for each.

The relationships between measurement units are embedded in the number unit, *Models You Can Count On*, where students explore conversions between measures of length within the Metric System. The measurement of area in both metric and Customary Systems is explicitly addressed in the unit *Reallotment*. Students also learn some simple relationships between metric and customary measurement units, such as 1 kilogram is about 2.2 pounds, and other general conversion rules to support estimations across different measurement systems. In *Reallotment*, *Made to Measure*, and *Packages and Polygons*, the concepts of volume and surface area are developed. Strategies that were applied to find area measurements in *Reallotment* are used to derive formulas for finding the volume of a cylinder, pyramid, and cone.

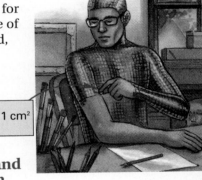

1 cm²

Visualization and Representation

Visualization and representation is a component of every geometry unit. In *Mathematics in Context*, this theme refers to exploring figures from different perspectives and then communicating about their appearance or characteristics.

In *Reallotment*, students use visualizations and representations to find the areas of geometric figures. They decide how to reshape geometric figures and group smaller units into larger, easy-to-count units. They also visualize and represent the results for changing the dimensions of a solid. In the unit *It's All the Same*, students visualize triangles to solve problems.

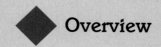
Student Assessment in Mathematics in Context

As recommended by the NCTM *Principles and Standards for School Mathematics* and research on student learning, classroom assessment should be based on evidence drawn from several sources. An assessment plan for a *Mathematics in Context* unit may draw from the following overlapping sources:

- **observation—As students work individually or in groups, watch for evidence of their understanding of the mathematics.**

- **interactive responses—Listen closely to how students respond to your questions and to the responses of other students.**

- **products—Look for clarity and quality of thought in students' solutions to problems completed in class, homework, extensions, projects, quizzes, and tests.**

Assessment Pyramid

When designing a comprehensive assessment program, the assessment tasks used should be distributed across the following three dimensions: mathematics content, levels of reasoning, and difficulty level. The Assessment Pyramid, based on Jan de Lange's theory of assessment, is a model used to suggest how items should be distributed across these three dimensions. Over time, assessment questions should "fill" the pyramid.

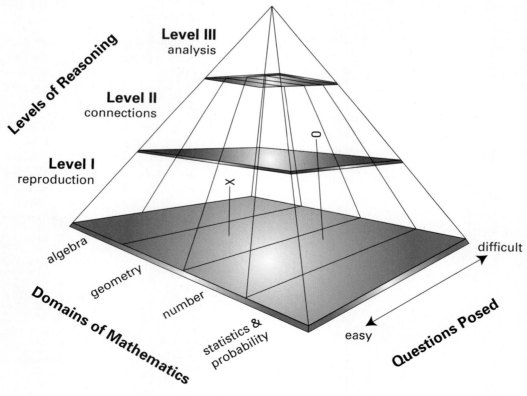

Levels of Reasoning

Level I questions typically address:

- recall of facts and definitions and
- use of technical skills, tools, and standard algorithms.

As shown in the pyramid, Level I questions are not necessarily easy. For example, Level I questions may involve complicated computation problems. In general, Level I questions assess basic knowledge and procedures that may have been emphasized during instruction. The format for this type of question is usually short answer, fill-in, or multiple choice. On a quiz or test, Level I questions closely resemble questions that are regularly found in a given unit, substituted with different numbers and/or contexts.

Level II questions require students to:

- integrate information;
- decide which mathematical models or tools to use for a given situation; and
- solve unfamiliar problems in a context, based on the mathematical content of the unit.

Level II questions are typically written to elicit short or extended responses. Students choose their own strategies, use a variety of mathematical models, and explain how they solved a problem.

Level III questions require students to:

- make their own assumptions to solve open-ended problems;
- analyze, interpret, synthesize, reflect; and
- develop one's own strategies or mathematical models.

Level III questions are always open-ended problems. Often, more than one answer is possible and there is a wide variation in reasoning and explanations. There are limitations to the type of Level III problems that students can be reasonably expected to respond to on time-restricted tests.

The instructional decisions a teacher makes as he or she progresses through a unit may influence the level of reasoning required to solve problems. If a method of problem solving required to solve a Level III problem is repeatedly emphasized during instruction, the level of reasoning required to solve a Level II or III problem may be reduced to recall knowledge, or Level I reasoning. A student who does not master a specific algorithm during a unit but solves a problem correctly using his or her own invented strategy may demonstrate higher-level reasoning than a student who memorizes and applies an algorithm.

The "volume" represented by each level of the Assessment Pyramid serves as a guideline for the distribution of problems and use of score points over the three reasoning levels.

These assessment design principles are used throughout *Mathematics in Context*. The Goals and Assessment charts that highlight ongoing assessment opportunities—on pages xvi and xvii of each Teacher's Guide—are organized according to levels of reasoning.

In the Lesson Notes section of the Teacher's Guide, ongoing assessment opportunities are also shown in the Assessment Pyramid icon located at the bottom of the Notes column.

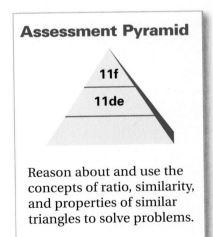

Assessment Pyramid

11f

11de

Reason about and use the concepts of ratio, similarity, and properties of similar triangles to solve problems.

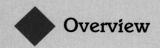

Goals and Assessment

In the *Mathematics in Context* curriculum, unit goals organized according to levels of reasoning described in the Assessment Pyramid on page xiv, relate to the strand goals and the NCTM *Principles and Standards for School Mathematics.* The *Mathematics in Context* curriculum is designed to help students demonstrate their understanding of mathematics in

each of the categories listed below. Ongoing assessment opportunities are also indicated on their respective pages throughout the Teacher's Guide by an Assessment Pyramid icon.

It is important to note that the attainment of goals in one category is not a prerequisite to the attainment of those in another category. In fact, students should progress simultaneously toward several goals in different categories. The Goals and Assessment chart is designed to support preparation of an assessment plan.

	Goal	Ongoing Assessment Opportunities	Unit Assessment Opportunities
Level I: Conceptual and Procedural Knowledge	**1.** Identify congruent and similar figures.	**Section A** p. 2, #1bc **Section C** p. 26, #9 abcd p. 31, #16a	**Quiz 1** #3 **Quiz 2** #2, 3a **Test** #1ab
	2. Recognize and use patterns in arrangements of congruent triangles.	**Section A** p. 4, #7ab p. 5, #8ab **Section B** p. 12, #7a	**Quiz 1** #2 **Test** #2ab
	3. Identify corresponding sides in similar figures.	**Section B** p. 13, #10ac p. 17, #18ab **Section C** p. 22, #1a, 2a	**Quiz 1** #1, 3 **Quiz 2** #1a **Test** #1abc
	4. Find a multiplication factor for similar figures	**Section B** p. 10, #3b p. 12, #7b, 8a p. 13, #10b **Section C** p. 22, #1b	**Quiz 1** #1, 2, 3 **Quiz 2** #1b, 3b **Test** #1c, 2a
	5. Determine unknown lengths in given similar figures.	**Section B** p. 13, #10ac **Section D** p. 41, #13b	**Quiz 1** #1, 3 **Quiz 2** #1c **Test** #1c, 2a

	Goal	Ongoing Assessment Opportunities		Unit Assessment Opportunities	
Level II: Reasoning, Communicating, Thinking, and Making Connections	**6.** Understand the relationship between parallel lines, equal angles, and slope.	**Section C** p. 23, Activity **Section E** p. 46, #4cd p. 48, #8		**Quiz 2** #3c	
	7. Prove that two triangles are similar.	**Section B** p. 21, For Further Reflection **Section C** p. 23, Activity p. 31, #16b		**Quiz 1** #3 **Quiz 2** #3c	
	8. Use properties of similar triangles to solve problems.	**Section B** p. 17, #18cd **Section C** p. 28, #11de p. 31, #16c **Section D** p. 41, #13c		**Quiz 1** #2, 3 **Test** #3, 4bd	

	Goal	Ongoing Assessment Opportunities		Unit Assessment Opportunities	
Level III: Modeling, Generalizing, and Non-Routine Problem Solving	**9.** Choose appropriate models and tools to solve geometric problems.	**Section E** p. 47, #5 p. 49, #10 **Section D** p. 41, #13a		**Test** #3	
	10. Reason about and use the concepts of ratio and similarity in solving problems.	**Section C** p. 28, #11f **Section D** p. 39, #11, 12		**Test** #4c	

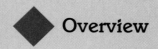

Materials Preparation

The following items are the necessary materials and resources to be used by the teacher and students throughout the unit. For further details, see the Section Overviews and the Materials section of the Hints and Comments column on the teacher page. Note: Some contexts and problems can be enhanced through the use of optional materials. These optional materials are listed in the corresponding Hints and Comments column.

Student Resources

Quantities listed are per student.

- **Letter to the Family**
- **Student Activity Sheets 1–6**

Teacher Resources

Quantities listed are per pair or group of students.

- **Long table (approximately one meter wide)**

Student Materials

Quantities listed are per student, unless otherwise noted.

- **Blank paper (one per pair of students)**
- **Compass**
- **Graph paper (three sheets)**
- **Centimeter graph paper (two sheets)**
- **Meter stick (one per pair of students)**
- **Rulers**
- **Scissors**
- **Straightedge**

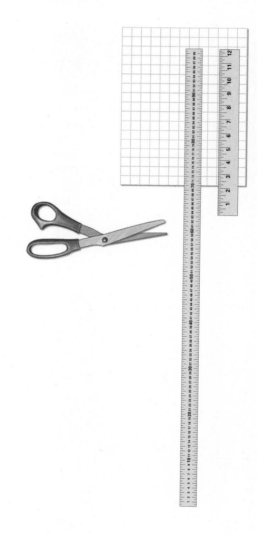

Student Material and Teaching Notes

◆ Contents

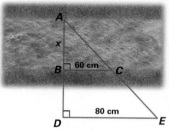

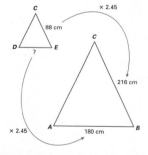

Dear Student,

Did you ever want to know the height of a tree that you could not climb? Do you ever wonder how people estimate the width of a river?

Have you ever investigated designs made with triangles?

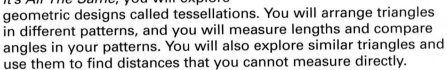

In this *Mathematics in Context* unit, *It's All The Same*, you will explore geometric designs called tessellations. You will arrange triangles in different patterns, and you will measure lengths and compare angles in your patterns. You will also explore similar triangles and use them to find distances that you cannot measure directly.

As you work through the problems in this unit, look for tessellations in your home and in your school. Look for situations where you can use tessellations and similar triangles to find lengths, heights, or other distances. Describe these situations in a notebook and share them with your class. Have fun exploring triangles, similarity, and tessellations!

Sincerely,

The Mathematics in Context Development Team

Section Focus

Students investigate similar shapes by tessellating congruent shapes to form large, similar shapes. In addition, they find algebraic rules for the number of triangles in each row of a triangle tessellation in relation to the total number of triangles that completely fill the large triangle. The properties of parallel lines, used to break down triangle tessellations, are reviewed. Parallel lines and congruent triangles were introduced in the unit *Triangles and Beyond*. Tessellations help students to understand similar triangles in several ways. They further develop the concept of ratio. This mathematical model also helps to find lengths of sides of similar triangles. And finally, the model helps students to develop a deeper understanding of the relationship between parallel lines and corresponding angles, which will be used later in the unit to formally prove similarity.

Pacing and Planning

Day 1: Triangles Forming Triangles		Student pages 1–4
INTRODUCTION	Activity, page 1	Arrange nine triangles into one large triangle and investigate the pattern made by the black triangles.
CLASSWORK	Problems 1–5	Compare tessellations of triangles, investigate rows formed by small triangles tessellating a large triangle, and identify families of parallel lines.
HOMEWORK	Problems 6 and 7	Reason about the relationship between the number of rows and the number of small triangles in a tessellated triangle.

Day 2: It's All in the Family (Continued)		Student pages 5–8
INTRODUCTION	Review homework.	Review homework from Day 1.
CLASSWORK	Problems 8 and 9	Verify a formula for the total number of triangles if a triangle is tessellated by n rows of small triangles, and design tessellations with different shaped pieces.
HOMEWORK	Check Your Work; For Further Reflection	Student self-assessment: Design new shapes using congruent figures.

Additional Resources: Additional Practice, Section A, Student Book pages 52 and 53

Materials

Student Resources

Quantities listed are per student.

- Letter to the Family
- **Student Activity Sheets 1** and **2**

Teachers Resources

No resources required

Student Materials

Quantities listed are per student.

- Compass
- Ruler
- Scissors
- Straightedge

* See Hints and Comments for optional materials.

Learning Lines

Characteristics and Properties of Shapes

Students review the concept of congruent triangles, without formal proof. They also review the concept of parallel lines and investigate how families of parallel lines can be used to tessellate a triangle.

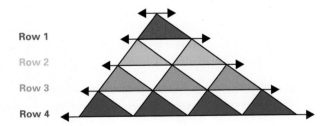

Geometric Relationships

Students investigate the relationship between the number of rows in a triangle tessellation and the number of triangles along each side of a triangle and find a formula to represent this relationship.

Transformations

The formal term is not used in this section. However, tessellations are an example of informal transformations such as flips, turns, and slides.

Use Visualization, Spatial Reasoning, and Geometric Modeling to Solve Problems.

Students use tessellations to find a relationship between an isosceles triangle and a rhombus, each tessellated by the same triangles.

At the End of This Section: Learning Outcomes

Students can say in their own words what parallel lines and congruent triangles are. They have informal knowledge of similar triangles without using the mathematical term yet. They have informally compared areas of similar shapes formed by different tessellations.

Notes

This is a fun activity. You might have students glue the symmetric design on a sheet of paper and display their work in the classroom. Allow enough time for students to rearrange the pieces so that all black parts that touch form triangles and to discover the symmetric design.

Tessellations

Triangles Forming Triangles

Cut out the nine triangles on **Student Activity Sheet 1**.

- Use all nine triangles to form one large triangle.

- Rearrange the nine triangles to form one large triangle so you form a black triangle whenever two triangles meet.

- Rearrange the nine triangles to form a symmetric pattern. How can you tell your arrangement is symmetric?

Reaching All Learners

Intervention

Remind students that all black parts that touch must form a triangle for the second and third parts of the instructions.

Solutions and Samples

Activity

Note that students do not have to make drawings.

Sample arrangements:

- Here is one large triangle.

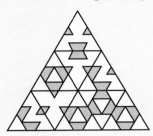

- A black triangle forms whenever two triangles meet.

- If an arrangement is symmetric, you can fold the triangle so that the two halves match exactly. The two halves are mirror images of each other.

Hints and Comments

Materials

Student Activity Sheet 1 (one per student); scissors (one pair per student)

Overview

Students arrange nine triangles into one large triangle. They investigate the pattern made by the black triangles.

About the Mathematics

One purpose of this activity is to introduce students in a concrete way to the idea of composing larger triangles from smaller triangles. This will be helpful since many of the problems later in the unit require students to use congruent triangles to tessellate a large triangle.

Comments About the Solutions

- It is possible to arrange the triangles so that the pattern is symmetric (see the third example in the Solutions column). If none of the students have a symmetric arrangement, you may want to challenge them to find one.

A Tessellations

Notes

A Tessellations

Tessellations

A **tessellation** is a repeating pattern that completely covers a larger figure using smaller shapes. Here are two tessellations covering a triangle and a **rhombus**.

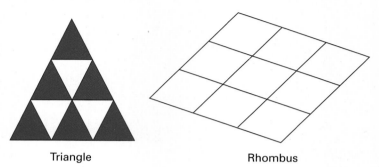

Triangle   Rhombus

1a You may need to be more specific and ask how many times bigger the area of the large triangle is than the area of the small triangle.

1c You may want to review the definition of *rhombus* by asking how we know the quadrilateral in the picture is a rhombus.

1. **a.** How does the area of the large triangle compare to the area of the rhombus?

   b. The triangle consists of nine **congruent** triangles. What does the word *congruent* mean?

   c. The rhombus consists of a number of congruent rhombuses. How many?

   d. You can use the blue and white triangles to cover or tessellate the rhombus. How many of these triangles do you need to tessellate the large rhombus?

   e. Can you tessellate a triangle with 16 congruent triangles? If so, make a sketch. If not, explain why not.

Assessment Pyramid

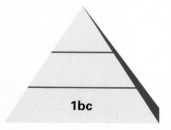

Identify congruent figures.

Reaching All Learners

Accommodation

It is helpful to have isometric dot paper available for problem 1e for those students who might have difficulty with the drawing.

Vocabulary Building

You may want to demonstrate the meaning of the word *congruent* by having students use a cardboard or paper triangle as a master copy for making tessellations. Students may also remember studying congruent figures that were made with stamps and stencils in the unit *Triangles and Beyond*.

Solutions and Samples

1. a. When you turn the large triangle and take out the color, it is half of the rhombus. To get the rhombus, just flip the turned triangle over.

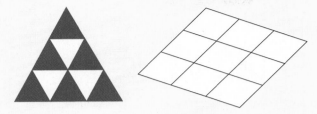

The area of the large triangle is half the area of the rhombus. Two large triangles form the rhombus.

b. Answers will vary. Sample responses:
- It describes figures that are exact copies of each other.
- It describes figures that would match up if you put one on top of the other.
- It describes figures with the same size and shape.

c. The large rhombus consists of nine congruent rhombuses.

d. Each small rhombus can be built with two congruent small triangles. You need

2 × 9 = 18 small triangles.

e. Yes, you can build a large triangle with 16 congruent small triangles by putting an extra row of seven triangles at the bottom. Here is a sketch of a triangle with 16 congruent triangles.

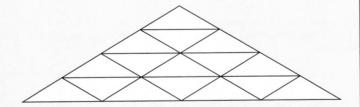

Hints and Comments

Materials

isometric dot paper, optional;
cardboard or paper triangle, optional

Overview

Students compare tessellations of a triangle and a rhombus that is double the size of the triangle. Students also explain the word *congruent*.

About the Mathematics

This unit formalizes the concepts of congruence and similarity. In the unit *Triangles and Beyond*, the term *congruent* is introduced with the informal definition "figures that are copies of each other." Students also saw rhombuses (parallelograms with four equal sides) in that unit. There a parallelogram was built from a triangle by rotating and translating its image, as shown below.

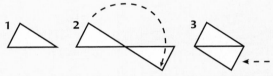

"Filling" a triangle with congruent triangles is called a *tessellation* of the triangle.

On this page, students are introduced to the rule that if n small triangles are along each side of a large triangle, the total number of small triangles tessellating the large triangle is n^2. Of course the formal rule is not mentioned yet.

Planning

You may want to answer problem 1 as a whole class discussion. Have students use their own words to describe the meaning of the word *congruent*. Problem 1e is an informal introduction to a general rule. In general, it is easier to show why a rule is <u>not</u> true, since you only need to provide one counter-example. This rule is true, but at this time do not expect formal proof: a drawing suffices. Discuss how different triangles made by different students all show that the triangle can be tessellated with 16 small triangles.

Extension

You may want to have students make large triangles out of 16 isosceles or equilateral small triangles and compare the results to their answer of problem 1e.

Notes

An overhead transparency copy of the tessellated triangle helps with the discussion of this page. Also review the definition of *parallel lines* with the students.

3a and **3b** If a prompt is needed, have students use their thumb or an index card to cover up the last two rows. Then ask what 4 has to do with these two rows. Then cover up the last row. Ask what 9 has to do with the first three rows.

3c If necessary, have students extend the sequence of 1, 4, 9, 16, …

Here is a large triangle tessellation.

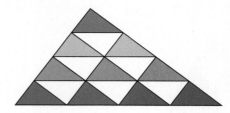

You can break it down by cutting rows along **parallel** lines.

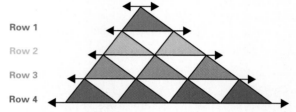

Row 1
Row 2
Row 3
Row 4

These lines form one **family of parallel lines**. There are other families of parallel lines.

2. How many different families of parallel lines are in this large triangle?

Here is the triangle cut along a different family of parallel lines.

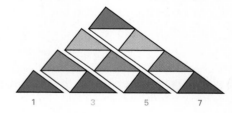

1   3   5   7

3. a. Explain the numbers below each row.

b. Explain what the sequence of numbers 1, 4, 9, 16 has to do with the numbers below each row.

c. Lily copied this tessellation but decided to add more rows. She used 49 small triangles. How many triangles are in Lily's last row?

Reaching All Learners

Intervention

Give students a copy of the tessellated triangle for problem 2. With a ruler, they could draw each family of parallel lines, using a different colored pencil for each family.

Extension

With problem 3c, using isometric dot paper, students could draw several rows of triangles and investigate to see if the pattern continues. Another possibility is to use plastic triangles to create a tessellated large triangle.

Solutions and Samples

2. There are three families of parallel lines.

3. a. The numbers below the strips show the numbers of congruent triangles in each row.

b. 1, 4, 9 and 16 show the total number of triangles:

1; 1 + 3 = 4; 1 + 3 + 5 = 9; 1 + 3 + 5 + 7 = 16

c. There are 13 triangles in the last row. Students may extend the patterns:

1   3   5   7   9   11   13   15   17   ....

1   4   9   16   25   36   49   64   .....

Hints and Comments

Materials

transparency of tessellation from problem 2, optional;
isometric dot paper, optional;
plastic triangles, optional;
ruler, optional;
colored pencils, optional

Overview

Students investigate the rows formed by the small triangles tessellating a large triangle. Students draw parallel lines to delineate rows of congruent triangles that fill a large triangle.

About the Mathematics

In the unit *Triangles and Beyond*, the concept of parallel lines is made explicit. In the same unit, parallel lines are constructed using a straightedge and a drawing triangle, as shown below:

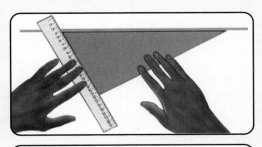

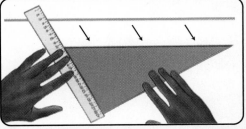

Planning

You may want to review how parallel lines can be drawn using a straightedge and a triangle.

Comments About the Solutions

2. Each side of the small triangle creates a family of parallel lines, which means there are three families of parallel lines.

3. Problem 3c is a reverse question to problem 1e on page 2. Both problems form an introduction to the general rule that if n small triangles are along each side of a large triangle, the total number of small triangles tessellating the large triangle is n^2. Students find the formula in problem 7b.

Tessellations

Notes

4a Some students may find it helpful to first mark the intersection points so they get the ruler in the correct position.

5 This can be difficult unless students have a strategy for creating parallel lines. Discuss some options with them such as using an index card or a plastic triangle with a 90-degree angle to align the ruler.

5a Ask, *How can you check the accuracy of your drawing?* All 25 small triangles should appear to be congruent.

It's All in the Family

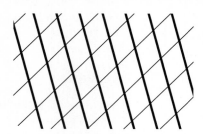

Here is a drawing, made with two families of parallel lines. It is the beginning of a tessellation of parallelograms.

4. **a.** On **Student Activity Sheet 2**, draw in a third family of parallel lines to form a triangle tessellation.

   b. Are the resulting triangles congruent? Why or why not?

   c. Did everyone in your class draw the same family of parallel lines?

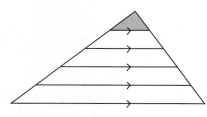

You can use one small triangle to make a triangle tessellation. All you need to do is draw the three families of parallel lines that match the direction of each side of the triangle.

This large triangle shows one family of parallel lines.

5. **a.** Here's how to finish this triangle tessellation. On **Student Activity Sheet 2**, use a straightedge to draw the other two families of parallel lines.

   b. How many small triangles are along each edge?

   c. How many small triangles tessellate the large triangle?

6. **a.** If the triangle in problem 5 had ten rows, how many triangles would be along each edge?

   b. How many small triangles would tessellate a triangle with ten rows?

7. **a.** Think about a large triangle that has *n* rows in each direction. How many small triangles would be along each edge of the large triangle?

   b. Write a formula for the total number of triangles to tessellate a triangle with *n* rows.

Assessment Pyramid

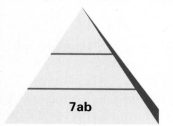

7ab

Recognize and use patterns in arrangements of congruent triangles.

Reaching All Learners

Intervention

For problems 6 and 7, a table showing the number of rows and the number of triangles for up to 10 rows helps students clearly see the pattern, and how the total number of triangles needed to tessellate would be expressed using *n*.

Solutions and Samples

4. a. There are two possibilities:

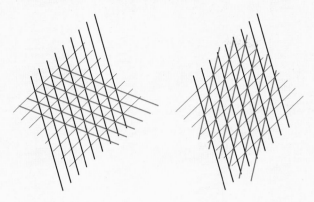

b. Yes, all triangles formed from one family of parallel lines are congruent. If you didn't use the same family, then you would have two different triangle sizes. The family of parallel lines uses the same triangle with some transformation like a flip or a glide or rotation.

c. Probably not since there are two ways to make the triangles.

5. a.

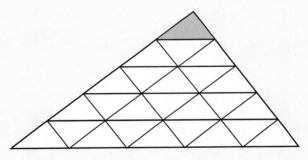

b. Five small triangles make up each edge.

c. 25 triangles all together tessellate the large triangle.

6. a. 10 triangles

b. 100 triangles

7. a. n triangles

b. The total number of triangles is $n \times n$, or n^2.

Hints and Comments

Materials

Student Activity Sheet 2 (one per student); straightedges (one per student); drawing triangles, optional (one per student)

Overview

Students draw three families of parallel lines that form a triangle tessellation. They further investigate the rows formed by the small triangles. They draw lines to delineate rows of congruent triangles that fill a large triangle. Students reason about the relationship between the number of rows and the number of small triangles in a tessellated triangle.

About the Mathematics

Families of parallel lines only form congruent triangles if in each "family" the lines are at the same distance from each other.

Planning

Students may work on the problems on this page individually or in small groups. Make sure you discuss the answers to problem 7b with students. Accept formulas in words or with the use of symbols. You may want to investigate with your students what happens if in problem 4, the lines in one "family" are all parallel but not at equal distances.

Comments About the Solutions

6. Students may draw the triangle and count the number of small triangles, or they may generalize using the pattern they noticed in problem 5.

7. This problem gives students the opportunity to generalize from the pattern they observed in problems 5 and 6. Students may remember how to use a variable to describe an answer from the unit *Building Formulas*. Another way of finding the total number of triangles in the tessellation is investigated in the unit *Patterns and Figures*.

A 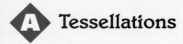 Tessellations

Notes

For some students, it is not obvious that triangles can be congruent if placed in different positions.
You may need to review this for some of them.

Laura used one triangle to make rows of congruent triangles.

She noticed very interesting things happen.

- Rows form parallel lines in three different directions.
- There is the same number of small triangles along each edge.

8. a. Make up your own large triangle tessellation using one small triangle.

8a A triangle cut from an index card or poster board is easier to use.

b. Verify that the formula you found in problem 7b works for this tessellation.

Tessellations can make beautiful designs. Here is a tessellation design based on squares. This tessellation consists of eight pieces using only two different shapes.

9 Make sure students understand that, for example, the two reddish-brown pieces in each square of the first design are congruent but are rotated or flipped.

9. a. How many total pieces do you need to make each of these tessellation designs? How many different shapes do you need?

i.   **ii.**   **iii.**

 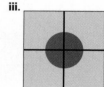

b. Design your own tessellation, based on squares, which consists of 16 pieces using exactly four different shapes.

Assessment Pyramid

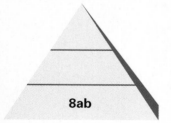

8ab

Recognize and use patterns in arrangements of congruent triangles.

Reaching All Learners

Accommodation

To help students "see" the different shapes in problem 9, you may want to cut out the different shapes and on an overhead projector show how they are pieced together.

Solutions and Samples

8. a. Students' designs will vary. Make sure the tessellations consist of congruent triangles and that an equal whole number of triangles fits along each side.

b. If the design was right, the formula found in problem 7b will work for this design.

9. a.

Figure	Total Pieces	Different Shapes
I	12	2
II	16	3
III	8	2

b. Designs will vary. Two samples:

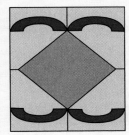 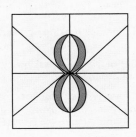

Hints and Comments

Materials

rulers (one per student);
drawing triangles, optional (one per student);
compasses (one per student)

Overview

Students verify the formula, total number of triangles $= n^2$, if a large triangle is tessellated by n rows of small triangles. They design their own tessellations using different-shaped congruent pieces.

Tessellations

Notes

Summary

Be sure *tessellation* and *congruent* figures are part of your vocabulary discussion.

 Summary

A *tessellation* is a repeating pattern that completely covers a large shape using identical smaller shapes.

Congruent figures are exact "copies" of each other. Two figures are congruent if they have the same size and the same shape.

When you use a small triangle to make a large triangle tessellation, interesting patterns occur.

2 rows, 4 triangles   3 rows, 9 triangles

- The number of triangles making up each row is the odd number sequence, 1, 3, 5…
- The total number of triangles making up the triangle is always a perfect square number, 1, 4, 9, 16, 25…
- The number of rows will tell you how many small triangles tessellate a large triangle; for example, a triangle with six rows needs 36 small triangles to make a tessellation.

You can make a tessellation using small shapes.

Kira completely covered this trapezoid using two shapes, a triangle and a hexagon.

Her tessellation consists of 21 pieces using 2 different shapes.

She used 14 congruent triangles and 7 congruent hexagons.

   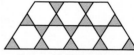

Trapezoid   Trapezoidal Tessellation

Reaching All Learners

Extension

If students have pattern blocks available to them, they could use the blocks to create tessellations. Another possibility is to investigate patchwork quilt designs to find tessellating patterns.

Writing Opportunity

As an alternative to this Summary, you might have students write their own summary of what they have learned so far. Their summaries should include the notions of congruent shapes (triangles), parallel lines, and tessellations of a large triangle by small triangles of the same shape.

Solutions and Samples

Hints and Comments

Materials

pattern blocks, optional

Overview

Students read the Summary, which reviews the main concepts covered in this section.

Planning

After students complete Section A, you may assign for homework appropriate activities from the Additional Practice section, located on pages 52 and 53 of the Student Book.

Notes

You can make a tessellation using families of parallel lines.

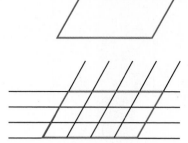

Logan used two families of parallel lines to create a tessellation for a large parallelogram. His tessellation consists of 12 small congruent parallelograms.

Check Your Work

1. **a.** Describe another way to identify congruent figures.

   b. Make two congruent shapes. Describe all the parts of the shape that are exactly the same.

2. Design a large triangle using four rows of congruent triangles.

1b and 2 Some students may need index card or card stock to cut out their shape and trace it to create congruent shapes.

Assessment Pyramid

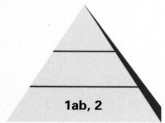

1ab, 2

Assesses Section A Goals

Reaching All Learners

Accommodation

Allow for a variety of strategies for creating the four rows of congruent triangles. Cutting out a triangle and copying it, using isometric dot paper, and using parallel lines are some of the options.

Solutions and Samples

Answers to Check Your Work

1. There are different correct answers.

   a. One example: Congruent figures can be placed on top of each other with an exact fit. Compare your answer with that of a classmate.

   b. Many different congruent shapes are possible. If placed on top of each other, the two shapes you made should fit exactly. Name side lengths and angles that have equal measures.

2. Here is one sample design using 4 rows and congruent triangles. Your design is probably different from this one.

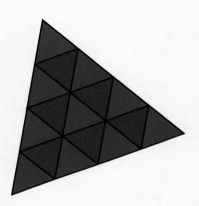

Hints and Comments

Materials

isometric dot paper, optional
index card or card stock, optional

Overview

Students use the Check Your Work problems as self-assessment. The answers to these problems are also provided in the Student Book, page 57. Students explain how congruent figures can be identified. They also solve problems dealing with large triangles that are built from smaller, congruent triangles.

Notes

Sketching can be difficult for some students, so have some optional support materials available such as isometric dot paper.

3 Some students may use other counting strategies, or they may apply what they learned from problem 7 on page 4. Encourage students to show or explain how they solved this problem.

For Further Reflection

Reflective problems are meant to summarize and discuss important concepts.

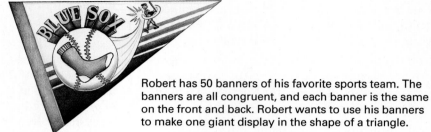

Robert has 50 banners of his favorite sports team. The banners are all congruent, and each banner is the same on the front and back. Robert wants to use his banners to make one giant display in the shape of a triangle.

3. a. Is it possible for Robert to arrange all 50 banners into a large triangle? If so, sketch the large triangle. If not, sketch a large triangular display that uses as close to 50 banners as possible.

   b. How many banners are along each edge? (Use your sketch from **a.**)

 For Further Reflection

Consider a large rectangle with dimensions 10 centimeters (cm) by 20 cm. Find different ways to tessellate this rectangle with smaller rectangles. For each tessellation, record the dimensions of the smaller rectangles. (Remember: A tessellation must completely cover the shape.)

Assessment Pyramid

3ab, ☐FFR

Assesses Section A Goals

Reaching All Learners

Intervention

With the For Further Reflection problem, students should check to see if their smaller rectangles actually work by drawing the large rectangle filled with the smaller rectangles.

Solutions and Samples

3. a. No, the number of small triangles must be a perfect square. So the closest Robert can get to using all 50 banners is to use 49.

b. There are seven banners along each edge. Here are two sample strategies:

- I made a sketch of the large banner. One small banner is left over.

- I counted the number of banners for each row and added them up. One banner would be left over.

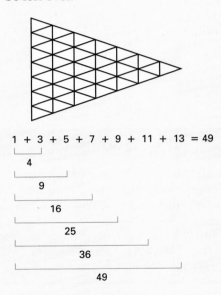

For Further Reflection

Sample tessellation:

An example of four 5 cm × 10 cm rectangles tessellating a 10 cm × 20 cm rectangle (not drawn to scale).

Hints and Comments

Materials

isometric dot paper, optional

Overview

Students use the Check Your Work problems as self-assessment. The answers to these problems are also provided on Student Book page 57.

Section Focus

Similar triangles are investigated in a preformal way with the help of enlargements and reductions. Students explored this concept in the unit *Ratios and Rates*. The ratio table is used here to help students organize calculations when finding lengths of corresponding sides of similar triangles. Students find that not all problems about similar triangles can be solved using tessellations. In this section, the **multiplication factor** is used to describe the relationship between shapes that are either an enlargement or a reduction of each other. A connection is made with percents to represent a multiplication factor. Students learn what a multiplication factor is; for example, 300% means the factor of enlargement is 3. In this section, no formal proof of similarity is expected of students yet, but the formal term is used.

Pacing and Planning

Day 3: More Triangles		Student pages 9–12
INTRODUCTION	Problems 1 and 2	Use the relationships among the side lengths of large triangles to find the small triangles that will tessellate them.
CLASSWORK	Problems 3–6	Find different triangles to tessellate a larger triangle and find factors of enlargement and reduction.
HOMEWORK	Problem 7	Describe restrictions for tessellating triangles and find a multiplication factor.

Day 4: Overlapping Triangles		Student pages 12–14
INTRODUCTION	Review homework.	Review homework from Day 3.
CLASSWORK	Problems 8–11	Use various strategies to determine unknown lengths in given similar triangles.
HOMEWORK	Problems 12 and 13	Solve problems by tessellating or by using a multiplication factor.

Day 5: The Bridge Problem (Continued)		Student pages 15–21
ACTIVITY	Review homework.	Review homework from Day 4.
CLASSWORK	Problems 14–19	Use various strategies to solve problems involving similar triangles.
HOMEWORK	Check Your Work	Student self-assessment: Identify similar triangles and solve problems using properties of similar triangles.

Day 6: Summary		Student page 21
INTRODUCTION	Review homework.	Review homework from Day 5.
ASSESSMENT	Quiz 1	Assesses Sections A and B Goals
HOMEWORK	For Further Reflection	Create similar triangles and describe their common properties.

Additional Resources: Additional Practice, Section B, pages 53 and 54

Materials

Student Resources

No resources required

Teachers Resources

No resources required

Student Materials

Quantities listed are per student.

• Rulers

* See Hints and Comments for optional materials.

Learning Lines

Characteristics and Properties of Shapes

Students learn another method to describe similar triangles, by way of a multiplication factor. They analyze overlapping triangles and identify corresponding sides. Then they use the relationship between those sides to find the length of an unknown side.

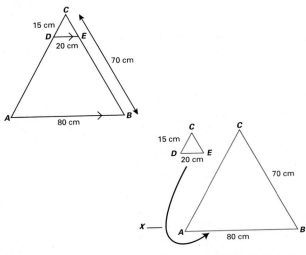

Geometric Relationships

Students further investigate the relationship between the ratios of side lengths and areas of similar triangles.

Transformations

Students review transformations as used in tessellations and identify equal angles.

Use Visualization, Spatial Reasoning, and Geometric Modeling to Solve Problems

Students choose the tessellation strategy for similar triangles or use the multiplication factor to find the ratio of corresponding sides in similar triangles to solve problems involving the dimensions of a ramp of a bridge. They use similar triangles to find the length of a book shelf in a triangle shaped bedroom under a roof top and make assumptions for missing information.

At the End of This Section: Learning Outcomes

Students choose between two strategies to solve problems involving similar triangles. They know how to use the ratio of corresponding sides, the multiplication factor. They understand that a shape is enlarged if the multiplication factor is greater than 1 and reduced if the multiplication factor is smaller than 1 but greater than zero. They can express multiplication factors as the ratio of corresponding sides, using fractions, whole numbers, and percents.

You may want to begin this section with a discussion on enlargement or reduction to see if your students have used a copy machine for this purpose or possibly enlarged a drawing in art class.

1 If prompting is needed, ask how many triangles are along each edge.

2b If any students have never used a ratio table, explain that they work just like equivalent fractions.

Enlargement and Reduction

More Triangles

This large triangle is partially tessellated. The dimensions of the large triangle are given.

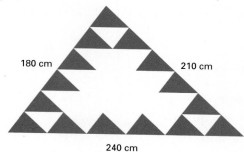

1. What are the lengths of the sides of the small triangle used in the tessellation?

2. **a.** Make a table like this one to record your answers to problem 1.

Lengths of Sides			
Small Triangle			
Large Triangle	180 cm	210 cm	240 cm

  b. Explain why this table is also a ratio table.

  c. Compare the small triangle to the large triangle. What do you notice?

  d. The large triangle is an enlargement of the small triangle. The **enlargement factor** is 6. Explain what this means.

Reaching All Learners

Intervention

Some students may have difficulty visualizing the small and large triangles used in these diagrams. You may want to have students draw the triangles separately or use different colors to outline the triangles in each diagram.

Vocabulary Building

It may help to explain that the *factor of enlargement* is the same as the multiplier between the side of the small triangle and the corresponding side of the large triangle.

Solutions and Samples

1. 30, 35, and 40 centimeters. Since there are six identical smaller triangles along each edge, you only need to divide the large dimension by 6.

2. a.

Small Triangle	30 cm	35 cm	40 cm
Large Triangle	180 cm	210 cm	240 cm

$\times 6$

   b. Sample explanation: I can work with the first pair of sides and manipulate them to attain the other side lengths.

$$\div 3 \quad \times 4 \quad \div 8$$

Small Triangle	30	10	40	5	35 (30 + 5)
Large Triangle	180	60	240	30	210 (180 + 30)

   c. Comparisons will vary. Sample comparisons:

   When you multiply the dimensions of the small triangle by 6, you will get the dimensions of the large triangle. The dimensions of the small triangle are $\frac{1}{6}$ of the size of the larger triangle. Thirty-six triangles will tessellate the large triangle, so the area of the small triangle is $\frac{1}{36}$ of the area of the large triangle.

   d. Explanations will vary. Sample explanations:

   - In the table, the numbers in the top row multiplied by 6 give the numbers in the bottom row. So the lengths of the sides of the large triangle are 6 times the lengths of the sides of the small triangle.

   - Six small triangles fit along each edge of the larger triangle. Enlarging each dimension of the small triangle by multiplying by 6 will produce the large triangle.

Hints and Comments

Materials

graph paper, optional (one sheet per student); colored pencils, optional (three colors per student)

Overview

Students use a drawing of a partially tessellated triangle to determine the measurements of the small triangles used in the tessellation. They use the relationships among the side lengths of large triangles to find the small triangles that will tessellate them, and then use ratios to determine unknown lengths of large triangles.

About the Mathematics

In the previous section, students discovered that when a large triangle is tessellated with smaller congruent triangles, the numbers of small triangles along the edges are always the same.

The ratio table is used here to help students organize computations and study constant relationships. In this case, the ratio of the lengths of corresponding sides in similar figures is constant.

In this section, connections can be made with the concept of factor of enlargement (or reduction) that was made explicit in the unit *Ratios and Rates*. The unit *It's All the Same* introduces students to similar triangles through the concept of tessellation. Tessellation helps students to understand similar triangles in several ways. It helps students to further develop the concept of ratio. Tessellation can be used as a mental model to find lengths in similar figures. Finally, it enables students to develop an understanding of the relationship between parallel lines and corresponding angles, which will be used to prove similarity in Section D.

Comments About the Solutions

2. Students may use the ratio table to make connections between the number of small triangles along each side and the relationship between the side lengths of the small and large triangles.

B Enlargement and Reduction

Notes

3a It may help to explain that there are infinite possibilities for tessellating triangles, but the ones found by dividing by the whole number common factors are easier to use.

4 You may want to discuss with students how this ratio table is organized and how it relates to the problem they are solving.

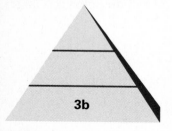

Find a multiplication factor for similar figures.

You can tessellate this triangle with small congruent triangles.

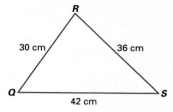

3. a. Find three different triangles that can tessellate △QRS. For each triangle, give the lengths of the sides and explain why it tessellates the large triangle.

b. For each tessellation, compare the large and small triangles to find the enlargement factor.

This small triangle can tessellate a large triangle with dimensions 30 cm × 40 cm × 50 cm.

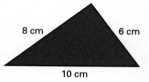

4. a. How many small triangles fit along each side of the large triangle?

b. Copy and complete this ratio table.

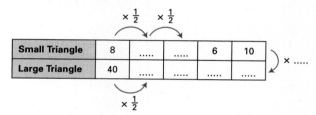

Small Triangle	8	.....	.....	6	10
Large Triangle	40	.....	.....	.....	.....

c. Which number shows the enlargement factor?

Before continuing, it is important to clarify some essential vocabulary of this unit.

Some of you probably have **enlarged** a special photograph to fit an 8 in. × 10 in. portrait frame.

You may have **reduced** a special photograph to fit into a wallet or small frame.

The **enlargement factor** or **reduction factor** is the number you need to multiply the dimensions of the original object.

The **multiplication factor** encompasses either an enlargement or a reduction.

Assessment Pyramid

Reaching All Learners

English Language Learners

To help students understand enlargement and reduction, it may help to have examples of simple shapes that have been enlarged or reduced. This could be done on a copy machine. The enlargement factor or reduction factor is the number used to multiply each dimension of the original object. Sometimes the factor is expressed as a percent.

Solutions and Samples

3. a. Answers will vary. Three sample responses:

Large Triangle	30 cm	36 cm	42 cm	Number of Triangles Along Each Side
Small Triangle, Example 1	10 cm	12 cm	14 cm	3
Small Triangle, Example 2	15 cm	18 cm	21 cm	2
Small Triangle, Example 3	5 cm	6 cm	7 cm	6

b. Answers will depend on the tessellations given in problem 3a. For the examples in the table, 3, 2, and 6 are the enlargement factors.

4. a. There are five small triangles along each edge.

b.

$\times \frac{1}{2}$ $\times \frac{1}{2}$

Small Triangle	8	4	2	6	10
Large Triangle	40	20	10	30	50

$\times 5$

$\times \frac{1}{2}$

c. The number 5 shows the enlargement factor. You have to multiply the sides of the small triangle by five to get the corresponding sides of the large triangle.

Hints and Comments

Overview

Students find different triangles that could be used to tessellate a given larger triangle. They start using the formal mathematical term *multiplication factor* to describe an enlargement or reduction

About the Mathematics

The strategy of tessellation is a powerful tool for developing students' understanding of similarity. A partial tessellation will give students visual support to find corresponding sides and unknown measurements. You might see students move from a concrete level to a more abstract level while they are solving these problems. For example, they may use rough sketches instead of accurate drawings or shorten counting strategies.

Planning

Students may work on these problems individually or in (small) groups.

Comments About the Solutions

3. Students can find their answers by tessellating the triangle or by understanding that there must be the same number of small congruent triangles along each side of the larger triangle.

B Enlargement and Reduction

Notes

5 Have rulers available for measuring each dimension to find the multiplication factor.

5 Students should notice that the ratio between the side lengths of the photographs is not the same as the ratio between the areas of the photographs.

6 Remind students to use what they learned in Section A. Ask, *How many copies of triangle DEC would fit along each edge?*

6 Students should start to see that they do not need to tessellate the entire triangle to complete the problem.

Enlargement and Reduction

Here is a photograph shown in different sizes.

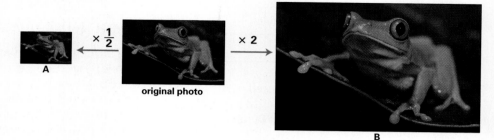

A $\times \frac{1}{2}$ original photo $\times 2$ B

The original photo was both enlarged and reduced.

5. **a.** What is the multiplication factor from the original photo to B?

   b. What is the multiplication factor from A to the original photo?

   c. What is the multiplication factor from A to B?

   d. A multiplication factor of two produces an enlargement of 200%. Explain why.

If the multiplication factor is a number from 0 to 1, the original figure is reduced in size.

If the multiplication factor is a number greater than 1, the original figure is enlarged.

In the drawing, $\triangle DEC$ can tessellate $\triangle ABC$.
In the small triangle, $DE = 40$ cm, $EC = 35$ cm, and $CD = 30$ cm.
In the large triangle, $AC = 270$ cm.

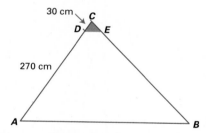

30 cm   C
D   E

270 cm

A   B

6. Use a ratio table to find the lengths of sides AB and BC.

Reaching All Learners

Intervention

To better understand the reduction factor, some students may need some review on multiplying by a fraction. Reinforce that finding one half of a number is the same as dividing by 2 or finding one third is the same as dividing by 3.

Making Connections

To reinforce relationships between percents and fractions, when reduction factors are discussed throughout this unit, encourage students to use percents as well as fractions.

Solutions and Samples

5. a. The multiplication factor from the original to B is two.

b. The multiplication factor from A to the original is two.

c. The multiplication factor from A to B is four.

d If you say the length and width of the original are 100% and you use a multiplication factor of two, the dimensions of the new photo are 200% of the original.

6. $AB = 360$ cm, and $BC = 315$ cm.

	Corresponding Side Lengths (cm)				
Small △DEC	30	10	5	40	35 (30 + 5)
Large △ABC	270	90	45	360	315 (270 + 45)

Hints and Comments

Overview

Students investigate photographs that are enlarged or reduced in size to find the multiplication factor.

About the Mathematics

Not all problems about similar triangles can be solved using tessellations. In this section, the *multiplication factor* is used. Students should understand what it means if the multiplication factor is smaller than one but greater than zero (the original figure is reduced in size), equal to one (the original figure is neither reduced or enlarged in size), or greater than one (the original figure is enlarged in size).

Planning

You may want to use photocopies of an interesting photograph with different enlargement or reduction factors to introduce the topic to students.

Extension

The context of tessellation provides an opportunity to investigate the relationships between side lengths and area. Ask, *How would you explain to someone that if the sides of a large triangle are five times larger than the sides of a smaller triangle, the area of the large triangle is not five times the area of the smaller triangle?* Students may answer the question using sample tessellations. In the example below, the shaded triangles are 5 times the area of one small triangle. Twenty-five of the small triangles would be needed to completely cover the large triangle.

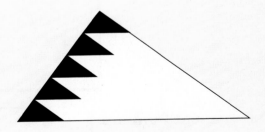

Notes

7b Some extra questions may be needed here to get students started. For example, *How long is side KM? Then 2 times what equals 7?*

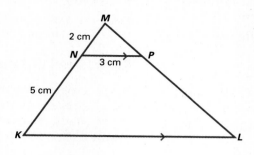

In the triangle, the markings indicate that sides *NP* and *KL* are parallel. As a matter of notation: *NP* ∥ *KL*.

7. a. Can you use △*NPM* to tessellate △*KLM*? If so, show the tessellation. If not, explain why you cannot.

    b. By which factor do you need to multiply △*NPM* in order to get △*KLM*?

    c. What is the difference between tessellating a triangle and enlarging a triangle?

Overlapping Triangles

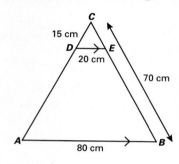

8 You may want students to write in their own words what corresponding sides are.

8a Remind students that the multiplier is the same for all the sides because of what they learned in Section A about tessellating the larger triangle.

Here are two new triangles. These triangles are overlapping triangles. Sometimes, it makes it easy to see the corresponding sides if you redraw the triangles separately.

The second drawing shows how, for example, side *DC* and side *AC* are **corresponding sides**.

8. a. What is the enlargement factor for these triangles?

    b. Use your answer from part **a** to find the length of side *AC*.

    c. What is the length of segment *AD*?

    d. What does $\frac{CB}{CE}$ equal?

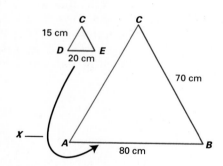

Assessment Pyramid

7ab, 8

Recognize and use patterns in arrangements of congruent triangles.

Find a multiplication factor for similar figures.

Reaching All Learners

Intervention

Drawing separate triangles and using arrows to indicate corresponding sides is a strategy that you will want students to use repeatedly for solving similar triangle problems.

For problem 8d, it may be necessary to remind some students that this fraction bar also indicates division.

Solutions and Samples

7. a. No. If you try to tessellate △KLM with △NPM, you will have either gaps or overlaps. The length of *MN* must divide evenly into that of *MK*.

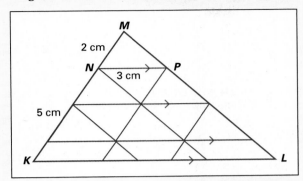

b. The multiplication factor from △NPM to △KLM is $3\frac{1}{2}$. This is like thinking, "What number can I multiply by 2 to get 7; (2 × ? =7)?" The answer is not a whole number, so you cannot tessellate △NPM with △KLM.

c. A tessellation uses complete triangles to fill up a larger triangle. In an enlargement, you manipulate all the dimensions by a multiplication factor to get a larger copy. You are not limited to whole numbers.

8. a. The enlargement factor is 4 (20 cm × 4 = 80 cm).

b. *AC* = 60 centimeters. Sample explanation:

Since four is the enlargement factor, I know I can multiply the length of side *DC* by four to find the length of side *AC*. *AC* = 4 × 15 =60 cm.

c. *AD* = 45 cm.

AD = AC − CD; AD = 60 cm − 15 cm, or 45 cm.

d. $\frac{CB}{CE}$ equals 4 since *CB* is four times as large as *CE* (the enlargement factor).

Hints and Comments

Overview

Students find that small triangles that have the same shape as a large triangle cannot always be used to tessellate the large triangle. The multiplication factor can be used in that case.

About the Mathematics

The multiplication factor is one way to represent the ratio between corresponding sides in a pair of similar triangles. The concept of similar triangles is made explicit in Section C on pages 24 and 25 of the Student Book. Students are not expected to prove similarity in this section. The formal mathematical term *corresponding sides* is used for triangles that are similar, even though the term *similar* is not yet used here. Note that formal symbols for parallel lines and triangles are used in this section.

Comments About the Solutions

7. This is the first time students are introduced to similar triangles in which the tessellating triangle is not obvious. Some students may now draw the conclusion that you can find the multiplication factor by dividing the length of a side in the large triangle by the length of the corresponding side in the small triangle. However do not tell students that they can find the multiplication factor in this way. Allow them to figure it out for themselves.

8. This problem is critical because it helps students to focus on separating the similar triangles, marking the known lengths of the sides and linking the corresponding sides of the similar triangles.

B Enlargement and Reduction

Notes

9 Have students use other vocabulary to explain what $\frac{AC}{CD} = 3$ means, such as the ratio of *AC* to *CD* is 3 to 1 or the multiplier between *AC* and *CD* is 3. Also ask how many copies of triangle *CDE* would fit along each side.

11 Drawing two separate triangles helps students realize that the length of *MN* is 12.

11 Ask, *How did you find the multiplication factor?* Sample response: Some students may say, "I started with 8 × some number = 12, and I saw that the number has to be 1.5." Other students may say, "You can find that number by dividing 12 by 8."

---

9. Find *DE*, if $\frac{AC}{CD} = 3$.

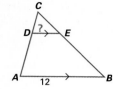

10. **a.** The length of side *KJ* in small △*KLJ* is 9. What is the length of the corresponding side *HJ* in the large triangle?

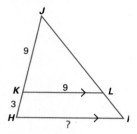

   b. What is the multiplication factor from △*KLJ* to △*HIJ*?

   c. Find the length of side *HI*, the side with the question mark.

11. For the two triangles below, find the length of the side with the question mark. (Hint: For the second figure, you may want to use a ratio table.)

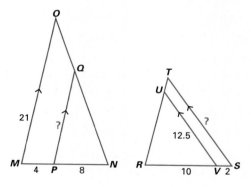

Assessment Pyramid

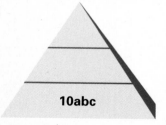

10abc

Find a multiplication factor for similar figures.

Determine unknown lengths in given similar figures.

Reaching All Learners

Intervention

For all the problems on this page, it is helpful to have the students draw two separate triangles, record the length on each side, and draw arrows from each side of the smaller triangle to the corresponding side in the larger triangle. Then have them write the enlargement factor (multiplier) on each arrow.

A mini-lesson on finding the multiplier may be needed. One possibility is to look at a few more examples where the multiplier is a whole number; then move to examples, such as the one on this page, 8 times what equals 12.

Solutions and Samples

9. $DE = 4$. The enlargement factor is 3, and $3 \times 4 = 12$.

10. a. $HJ = 3 + 9 = 12$

   b. Think about $9 \times ? = 12$ to find the multiplication factor; which is $\frac{12}{9} = 1\frac{3}{9} = 1\frac{1}{3}$. Check that $9 \times 1\frac{1}{3} = 12$.

   c. $HI = 12$. The corresponding side of KL is HI. $9 \times 1\frac{1}{3} = 12$.

11. For the first figure:

$PQ = 14$. Sample strategies:

- Use a ratio table with a goal to build up to 21.

Small Triangle	8	4	2	14
Large Triangle	12	6	3	21

- Find corresponding sides and use a multiplication factor.

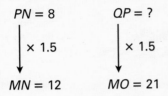

The multiplication factor is $\frac{12}{8} = 1\frac{4}{8} = 1\frac{1}{2}$, or 1.5.

Find the length of PQ by calculating $21 \div 1.5 = 14$.

For the second figure:

$ST = 15$. Students could organize the information in a ratio table, as shown below.

	÷ 2	÷ 2	2.5 + 10	
△ RVU	10	5	2.5	12.5
△ RST	12	6	3	15

3 + 12

Hints and Comments

Overview

Students use various strategies to determine unknown lengths in given similar triangles.

About the Mathematics

In this unit, students learn several methods they can use to find unknown lengths in similar triangles. Students are not expected to master all strategies. However in order to be able to choose one of the methods, students have to understand how each can be applied. Students can then choose one method when they solve a problem. In this section, students use the idea of the multiplication factor. Students who need more visual support may prefer making a drawing. Some students may feel more comfortable using the ratio table. The advantage of using this table is that unknown lengths can be found not only by using the multiplication factor but also by using other relationships.

Planning

You may want to have students work in small groups on problems 9 and 10. Discuss their answers and strategies later in class.

Comments About the Solutions

10. c. Students may realize that since $JK = KL$, HI will equal JH. This is apparent when the triangles are drawn separately. Some students may realize that they do not need to calculate and use the multiplication factor.

B Enlargement and Reduction

Notes

The Bridge Problem

Here is a side view of a bridge that Diedra drives across as she travels to and from work. (Note: The drawing is not to scale.)

As shown in the diagram below, when Diedra's car is 50 meters (m) up the ramp, she estimates she is about 3 m above ground level. She drives another 400 m and reaches the bridge.

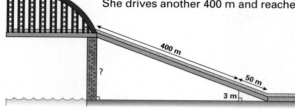

12. What is the height of the bridge above the ground? In the diagram, this distance is represented by the ? mark. Explain how you found your answer.

12 Careful reading is crucial here for students to note that the length of the ramp is 450 meters, not 400 meters.

13 Allow students to use their own strategies to solve this problem. If they have difficulty, you might encourage them to use a partial tessellation to check their answers.

Pete drew this diagram to start his solution of problem 12.

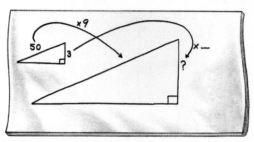

13. Pete wrote "×9" next to one of the arrows to indicate the enlargement factor. How did he decide that he needed to multiply by nine?

Reaching All Learners

Intervention

Encourage students to make a sketch of problem 12, labeling the length of the ramp and the height of the bridge, so they can use it when doing number 14 on the next page.

Solutions and Samples

12. 27 meters. Explanations will vary. Sample explanations:

I already know that the car is 3 meters high after driving 50 meters up the ramp and that the ramp is 450 meters in length. If I tessellate with the small triangle, I can fit eight more triangles on the side of the ramp. A total of nine triangles will fit along the base of the triangle. So the height of the bridge is 3 × 9, or 27 meters.

The length of the ramp is 450 meters, and 450 divided by 50 equals nine. Nine small triangles will fit along the side of the ramp. And so nine triangles will also fit along the height of the ramp. Each small triangle has a height of 3 meters. So the height of the bridge is 3 × 9, or 27 meters.

13. Answers will vary. Sample response:

The small triangle has a length of 50 meters up the ramp. The entire ramp is 450 meters long. 450 divided by 50 equals 9, so nine triangles would fit along the ramp. Nine triangles would also fit along the other two sides, so you can multiply the length of each side of the small triangle by 9 to get the length of the corresponding side in the large triangle.

Hints and Comments

Overview

Students find distances, such as the height of a bridge. They solve problems by tessellating or by using a multiplication factor.

Planning

For those students who found it difficult to solve the problems on the previous pages, the same type of problem is now reviewed within a context. Other students are able to work through the problems on this page without any guidance, choosing their own strategy. A common misconception is that for the total length of the ramp, 400 m is used instead of 450 m.

Comments About the Solutions

13. Students may respond that the small triangle is enlarged nine times in all directions.

B Enlargement and Reduction

Notes

If assistance is needed, ask what part of the right triangle formed by this new ramp corresponds to the 2-m side of the smaller triangle. They must note that both ends of the bridge are the same height. Then they should be able to find the multiplier.

16 If you have a transparency of triangle *ABC* and a color transparency of the reduced triangle, you can show how the triangles both have the same angle measures and the opposite sides are parallel by moving the small triangle around inside the original triangle.

You may want to suggest to students to label the new triangle *DEF*.

Richard drives up the other side of the bridge. As shown in the diagram, when Richard's car is 40 m up the ramp, he estimates that he is about 2 m above the ground. Both ends of the bridge are the same height. (Note: The diagram is not drawn to scale.)

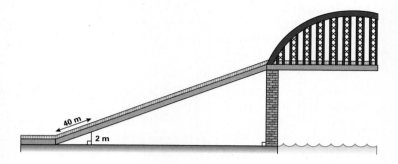

14. **a.** What is the length of the ramp at this end of the bridge?

   b. Which driver, Diedra or Richard, is driving on a steeper ramp?

15. Describe two methods for finding the multiplication factor for problem 12.

16. In your notebook, carefully copy △*ABC*. Create a new triangle that is similar to △*ABC* with a multiplication factor of 50%.

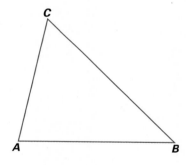

Reaching All Learners

Intervention

For some students you may need to review some benchmark fractions and percents, for example, 50% and $\frac{1}{2}$. By now most students should be flexible in changing from one representation to the other.

Accommodation

For problem 16, if tracing seems to be a problem for any students, have a copy ready for them to use and a ruler for all students. Some students have trouble doing the arithmetic needed for this problem. You may consider having them use a calculator.

Solutions and Samples

14. a. 540 meters. Sample strategy:

From problem 10, we know that the bridge is 27 meters high. Using a ratio table we can find that the ramp is 540 meters long.

$\times$ 13.5

2	27
40	540

b. Diedra is driving on the steeper ramp. Sample explanation:

Since the height is the same on both sides of the bridge but the ramp is shorter on Diedra's side (450 m versus 540 m), it must be steeper.

15. The multiplication factor is 9. Sample strategies:

- The small triangle can be used to tessellate the large triangle. Nine triangles will fit along each side, so the multiplication factor must be nine.

- The total length of the ramp is 450 meters, and $450 = 50 \times 9$, so 9 is the multiplication factor.

16. Check that the sides of the new triangle, drawn in $\triangle ABC$ or next to $\triangle ABC$, are half the sides of $\triangle ABC$.

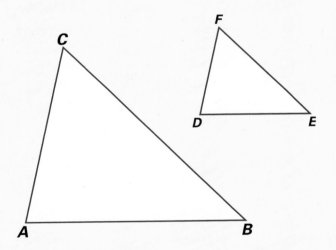

Hints and Comments

Materials

rulers (one per student);
drawing triangles, optional, (one per student);
calculators, optional (one per student);
copy of triangle for problem 16, optional

Overview

Students find the length of the ramp at the other end of the bridge. Then they compare the steepness of both ramps. They choose their own strategy when solving context problems.

About the Mathematics

The concept of similar triangles is made explicit in Section C. In this section, we do not expect students to prove two triangles are similar before solving a problem.

Comments About the Solutions

15. Here the two strategies to find a multiplication factor are compared. Discuss with students why finding the multiplication factor by dividing the length of a side in the large triangle by the length of the corresponding side in the small triangle always works and the strategy using tessellations does not always work.

16. The formal term *similar* is used here without really telling students what it means. You may ask for their own definition of the term *similar* here. Ask students how they know their drawing is correct.

B Enlargement and Reduction

Notes

17a Drawing the two triangles separately and drawing arrows to the corresponding sides helps students realize that that they cannot use 0.6 and 1.8 to find the multiplier.

17b Looking at a meter stick will enable some students to make a reasonable estimate for the width of a book. Others may just need to be reminded that 100 centimeters equals 1 meter.

You may want to discuss the assumptions needed to solve the problem on this page with your students. Ask, *What are the dimensions of a book?* You may want to measure some books in your classroom to get a general idea of possible dimensions.

Joseph's Bedroom

Joseph's bedroom is the entire top floor of his house. He wants to put up a shelf for his books, as shown in the drawing.

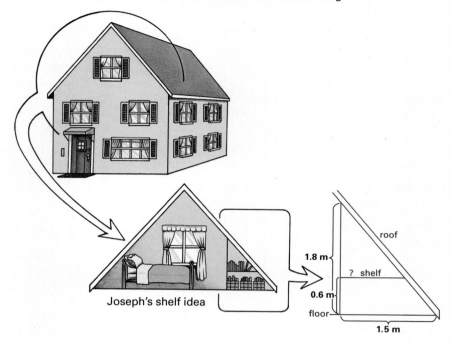

Joseph's shelf idea

17. **a.** What is the length of the shelf indicated by the question mark?

b. How many books will be able to fit on this shelf? Be sure to record any assumptions you make as you solve this problem.

Reaching All Learners

Extension

Students may enjoy building a model of this problem to see how close to the end of the shelf under the roof they can place books.

Intervention

Students may need to be encouraged to convert meters to centimeters (or decimeters) to get rid of the decimal point in the given numbers. Recall that 1m = 10 dm and 1 dm =10 cm or 1 m = 100 cm. Students may remember this strategy from earlier units.

Solutions and Samples

17. a. The shelf is 1 meter long. Strategies will vary. Sample strategy:

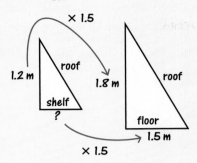

b. Answers will vary. Sample response:

If every book is 2 cm wide, Joseph's shelf is wide enough for 50 books. However, some will be too tall to fit in the corner. If Joseph's books are 20 cm tall, then only about 80 cm of the shelf can be used. Then Joseph can put 40 books on the shelf.

Hints and Comments

Overview

Students apply what they have learned so far while finding the length of a book shelf. They learn to make assumptions if, in a realistic problem, the information provided is not enough.

About the Mathematics

Students sometimes need to make assumptions (and write them down!) when solving realistic problems. It is important to emphasize the need for a reasonable estimate—not every assumption will do.

Comments About the Solutions

17. b. Since all dimensions are measured in centimeters, the dimensions of the book should also be given in cm.

B Enlargement and Reduction

Notes

Enlargement or reduction of a shape produces two shapes that are **similar** to one another. Often the similar shapes are **similar triangles**.

△*ABC* and △*DEC* (from problem 8) are similar triangles. The arrows connect the sides of the small triangle to the corresponding sides of the large triangle. The multiplication factor is the ratio of the corresponding sides.

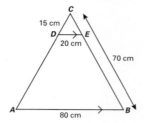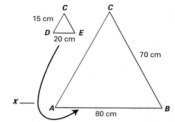

18. a. Which side corresponds to side *BC*?

b. Which side corresponds to side *AB*?

c. What is the multiplication factor from △*ABC* to △*DEC*?

d. What is the multiplication factor, from △*DEC* to △*ABC*, expressed as a percent?

Here are the top three floors of a pyramid building.

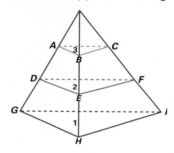

The multiplication factor from △*ABC* to △*DEF* is 2.

19. a. How does the area of floor *DEF* compare to the area of floor *ABC*?

b. What is the enlargement factor from floor 3 (*ABC*) to floor 1 (*GHI*)?

18d If necessary, prompt students to recall that 1 is equal to 100% and 2 is equal to 200%; then they should be able to calculate the percent for a factor of 4.

19 Encourage students to use the invaluable problem solving strategy of making a model if they are not sure how to do this.

They can draw any triangle and then make a second triangle with an enlargement factor of 2 and then of 3 and compare the areas. With luck, some student will think of tessellating the enlarged triangles to see how many times bigger the area is.

Assessment Pyramid

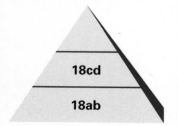

Solve problems involving similar triangles.

Identify corresponding sides in similar figures.

Reaching All Learners

Intervention

For problem 19, have a display of a tessellated triangle from Section A, such as the one on page 3 or the one in the Summary on page 6, to show how it is possible to use the tessellated triangle to answer problem 19.

Vocabulary Building

Students are familiar with comparing many things in terms of their similarities and differences in their language arts and social studies classes. In mathematics, however, similarity has a precise definition. For example, students might say that any triangles are "similar" since they share common features: three sides, three angles. and so on. However, the mathematical definition for similar triangles defines two triangles as similar if their corresponding angles are equal. This definition is made explicit on pages 24 and 25.

Solutions and Samples

18. a. Side *EC* corresponds to side *BC*.

b. Side *DE* corresponds to side *AB*.

c. The multiplication factor from $\triangle ABC$ to $\triangle DEC$ is $\frac{1}{4}$.

d. The multiplication factor in percents from $\triangle DEC$ to $\triangle ABC$ is 400%.

19. a. $\triangle ABC$ can tessellate $\triangle DEF$ and two small triangles will fit along each side of $\triangle DEF$. The total number of triangles is four, which means the area of $\triangle DEF$ is four times the area of $\triangle ABC$.

b. If you assume the layers of the pyramid building all have the same height, the enlargement factor from floor 1 to floor 3 is 4.

Hints and Comments

Overview

Students solve formal problems involving similar triangles. They compare the area of two similar triangles.

About the Mathematics

More and more formal mathematical language is used throughout the unit. Note that not all similar shapes are triangles. For example, all circles are similar shapes, and all squares are similar shapes.

Enlargement and Reduction

Notes

Discuss with students how the properties of tessellating triangles are related to the enlargement factor or reduction factor and similar triangles.

Tessellating Triangles

You can always tessellate a large triangle into smaller congruent triangles. It is not necessary to complete the tessellation.

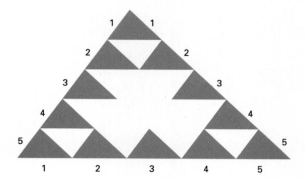

- When you know the dimensions of the large triangle and the number of triangles along each edge, you can find the dimensions of the small triangles.

- When you know the dimensions of the small triangle and the number of triangles along each edge, you can find the dimensions of the large triangle.

Reaching All Learners

Study Skills

Before looking at the Summary, ask students to review Section B and write down what they think are the important ideas in the section.

After discussing this in small groups, ask students to look at the Summary. What topics from the Summary were included on their list? Does the Summary include items not on their list? Do they have items that were not in the Summary? This strategy helps students review, helps them develop the ability to identify important ideas, ensures that they actually read the Summary, and helps them appreciate the value of the Summary section.

Hints and Comments

Overview

Students read the Summary, which reviews the main concepts covered in this section.

Enlargement and Reduction

Notes

For many similar triangle problems, a combination of both methods can be useful: sketching the two triangles, drawing arrows to show the corresponding sides, and then writing a ratio table to solve for the unknown lengths. Discuss strategies for putting the side lengths in the correct place in the ratio table.

Overlapping Triangles

In similar figures, you can find the multiplication factor if you know the lengths of two corresponding sides. You can use that factor to find any unknown lengths. A table helps to organize and calculate missing lengths.

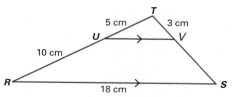

Multiplication Factor: 3	Corresponding Side Lengths of △TUV and △TRS		
Small △TUV	5	3	....
Large △TRS	15	....	18

× 3

This section contains two methods for organizing information about similar triangles.

- Sketch the two triangles and draw arrows to show the corresponding sides. Find the multiplication factor and use it to find unknown lengths.

- Make a ratio table for the corresponding sides.

Solving Problems

When you have a description of a situation, begin by making a drawing and labeling the side lengths you know. Then look for similar triangles so you can carefully compute the multiplication factor.

Reaching All Learners

Intervention

Discuss how important it is to check your answer to make sure it is reasonable. If the missing number is in the large triangle, it must be larger than the corresponding side in the small triangle. If the missing number is a side of the small triangle, it must be smaller than the corresponding side of the large triangle. A common error is to always multiply instead of remembering to divide if the side of the small triangle is missing.

Hints and Comments

Overview

Students read the Summary, which reviews the main concepts covered in this section.

Planning

After students complete Section B, you may assign for homework appropriate activities from the Additional Practice section, located on pages 53 and 54 of the Student Book.

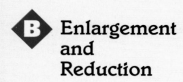

1c If a hint is needed, have students check the multiplication factor for each side.

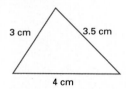

1. **a.** Find three different triangles that tessellate △ABC. Give the dimensions for each of your triangles.

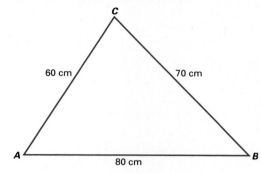

   b. Write a rule to find the sides of the triangles in **a.**

   c. Decide whether each triangle below can tessellate △ABC; justify your answers.

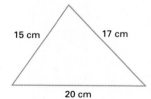

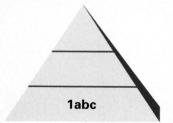
Reaching All Learners

Intervention

If any student has difficulty with finding the triangles that tessellate, have them review the Summary on page 18.

Solutions and Samples

Answers to Check Your Work

1. **a.** Here are three triangles that tessellate $\triangle ABC$ (60 cm, 70 cm, 80 cm).

   6 cm, 7 cm, 8 cm (divided original by 10);

   12 cm, 14 cm, 16 cm (doubled the previous); and

   30 cm, 35 cm, 40 cm (took half of original.)

   You probably have different size triangles; check that the multiplication factor is the same for all corresponding sides.

   b. Here is one possible rule.

   Find the common factors of the three side lengths of $\triangle ABC$. Then divide each side length by a common factor to find a smaller triangle that will tessellate $\triangle ABC$.

   c. The first triangle can tessellate $\triangle ABC$, since 20 of those triangles would fit along each side of $\triangle ABC$. The second triangle cannot tessellate $\triangle ABC$. Copies of this triangle do not fit along each side of $\triangle ABC$ the same number of times. The small base (20 cm) fits four times along the base (80 cm) of $\triangle ABC$, but the 17-cm side does not fit four times along the 70 cm side because 4×17 cm is not 70 cm.

Hints and Comments

Overview

Students use the Check Your Work problems as self-assessment. The answers to these problems are also provided on Student Book pages 58 and 59.

Notes

For Further Reflection

Have a variety of supplies available for students to create similar triangles: rulers, protractors, poster paper or index cards, and so forth.

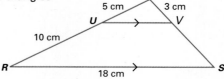

2. **a.** Name two similar triangles in this figure.

b. Use any method you want to find the length of side *TS*. Show your work.

3. Each of the figures has two similar triangles. Describe a way to find the multiplication factor and then find the multiplication factor. (Note: The figures are not drawn to scale.)

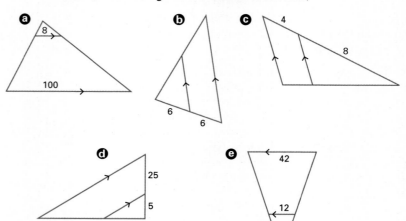

For Further Reflection

Create two similar triangles. Describe important features common to both shapes.

Assessment Pyramid

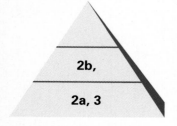

2b,

2a, 3

Assesses Section B Goals

Reaching All Learners

Intervention

For the problems on this page, you may need to remind some students to draw the two triangles separately and draw arrows to the corresponding sides.

Solutions and Samples

2. a. Here is one possible response.

△*RST* is similar to △*UVT*.

If your answer is different, make sure that the letters match up;
R ⟷ *U*, *S* ⟷ *V* and *T* ⟷ *T*.

b. The length of side *TS* is 9 cm. Here are two different strategies.

Using a tessellation:

Three copies of small △*UVT* fit perfectly along each side of △*RST*. This means the length of side *TS* is 9 cm (3 × 3 cm).

Using the multiplication factor:

UT = 5 cm and *RT* is 15 cm; the multiplication factor is 3.

3. Here are some ways to find the multiplication factors. Your method might be different.

a. The corresponding sides are 8 and 100.

$8 \xrightarrow{\times\ ?} 100$

Doing this in one step would be like dividing 100 by 8. The multiplication factor is 12.5.

b. The large triangle is divided into two equal parts, so the multiplication factor is two.

c. The corresponding sides are 8 and 12 (4 + 8). Then figure out what number times 8 equals 12. That number is 1.5 (or $1\frac{1}{2}$).

d. The corresponding sides are lengths of 5 and 30 (25 + 5). The smaller side divides evenly into the larger (30 ÷ 5 = 6). This means exactly six small triangles will fit along the edge. The multiplication factor is 6.

e. The corresponding sides are 12 and 42. 42 ÷ 12 = 3.5; the multiplication factor is 3.5 (or $3\frac{1}{2}$).

Hints and Comments

Overview

Students use the Check Your Work problems as self-assessment. The answers to these problems are also provided on Student Book pages 58 and 59.

For Further Reflection

Student drawings will vary. Check that both triangles are similar and check for neatness. A straightedge should be used for the drawings. Note that congruent triangles are also similar, with a multiplication factor of 1.

Sample description:

- The corresponding sides in my triangles are… and….

- (triangles overlapping) The sides of the triangle that are not overlapping are parallel.

Section Focus

In this section the concept of similar shapes is formalized. Formal mathematical notations and formal mathematical language are used. Students create similar and non-similar triangles with specified dimensions and observe that similar triangles have equal angle measures. In the previous sections, students were not expected to prove triangles were similar; in this section, they learn how to do that. There are two ways to prove that two triangles are similar.

- **Two triangles are similar if all corresponding sides have the same ratio. In order to draw this conclusion, you have to know the ratios of all corresponding sides.**
- **Two triangles are similar if all the corresponding angles are equal. To draw this conclusion, it is sufficient to know the measurements of two corresponding angles of each triangle.**

Pacing and Planning

Day 7: Similar Shapes		Student pages 22–25
INTRODUCTION	Problems 1 and 2	Investigate other shapes that are similar and the relationship between corresponding angles.
ACTIVITY	Activity, page 23	Draw triangles using a compass and straightedge, and investigate the relationships among corresponding sides.
CLASSWORK	Problems 3 and 4	Use properties of similar triangles to determine whether or not triangles are similar.
HOMEWORK	Problems 5 and 6	Determine the validity of an "If …, then…" statement and its inverse.

Day 8: Similar Shapes (Continued)		Student pages 25–28
INTRODUCTION	Problems 7 and 8	Verify properties of similar triangles using the sum of the angle measures in a triangle.
CLASSWORK	Problem 9 and 10	Determine whether or not pairs of shapes are similar and why.
HOMEWORK	Problem 11	Apply properties of similar triangles to solve problems.

Day 9: Angles and Parallel Lines		Student pages 29–31
INTRODUCTION	Review homework.	Review homework from Day 8.
ACTIVITY	Activity, page 29	Investigate the relationship between angles created by parallel lines.
CLASSWORK	Problems 12–14	Identify similar triangles and unknown side lengths.
HOMEWORK	Problem 15	Identify related figures.

Day 10: You Don't Have to Get Your Feet Wet		Student pages 31–34
INTRODUCTION	Problem 16	Determine the width of a river using the properties of similar triangles.
CLASSWORK	Check Your Work	Student self-assessment: Identify corresponding parts of similar triangles and find missing side lengths for similar triangles.
HOMEWORK	For Further Reflection	Describe various geometric terms using words and diagrams.

Additional Resources: Additional Practice, Section C, Student Book page 54

Materials

Student Resources

Quantities listed are per student.

- **Student Activity Sheets 3 and 4**

Teachers Resources

No resources required

Student Materials

Quantities listed are per student, unless otherwise noted.

- Compass
- Ruler or straightedge

* See Hints and Comments for optional materials

Learning Lines

Characteristics and Properties of Shapes

The notion of acute, obtuse and right angles is reviewed. Students review how parallel lines intersected by another straight line show angles with equal measures. This concept was addressed earlier, in the unit *Triangles and Beyond*. Students learn that all circles are similar shapes and all squares are similar shapes, but not all rectangles are.

At the End of This Section: Learning Outcomes

Students know formal rules to prove whether or not triangles are similar. They can choose their own strategy to solve problems involving similar triangles. They can identify equal angles produced by parallel lines and an intersecting line.

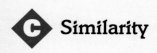
Notes

Several examples of similar figures (triangles, rectangles, hexagons, and so forth) provide good visuals for introducing this section on similarity. Copies made from card stock or heavy paper can be used to demonstrate the congruent angles and the corresponding sides.

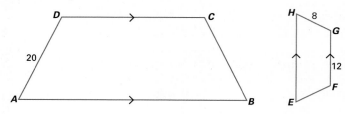

Similarity

Similar Shapes

Two figures are similar if they have identical shapes—not necessarily the same size. The lengths of corresponding sides are related through a multiplication factor.

These two figures are similar.

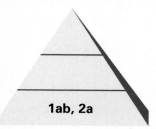

1. **a.** Which are the four pairs of corresponding sides?

   b. What is the multiplication factor from trapezoid *ABCD* to trapezoid *HEFG*?

   c. What is the length of *DC*?

   d. What are the corresponding angles?

A matter of notation:

- If figure *ABCD* is similar to figure *HEFG*, then *ABCD* ~ *HEFG*.
- The order of the letters relates to corresponding angles and sides.
- The angle at vertex *A*, written ∠*A* for short, is written as ∠*DAB* or ∠*BAD*; similarly ∠*D* can be written as ∠*GDE* or ∠*EDG*.

In similar shapes, corresponding angles have equal measures. Suppose △*ABC* ~ △*CDE*.

2. **a.** Which are the corresponding sides? (Hint: Make a sketch of the two triangles.)

   b. Name the corresponding angles.

   c. Which angle corresponds to ∠*BCA*?

2 Some students may need copies of similar triangles in order to do this problem.

Assessment Pyramid

1ab, 2a

Identify corresponding sides in similar figures.

Find a multiplication factor for similar figures.

Reaching All Learners

Intervention

A strategy for helping students who have difficulty identifying corresponding sides is to have them cut out copies of two similar figures. Then match up the corresponding angles (they are congruent). Then match up the corresponding sides when the shapes are placed in the same orientation. The corresponding sides are between the two pairs of corresponding angles. If the two figures are placed in the same orientation, these sides will be parallel. Also, the longest side corresponds to the longest side, and the shortest side corresponds to the shortest side.

Solutions and Samples

1. **a.** The four pairs of corresponding sides are:

   $AB - HE$

   $BC - EF$

   $DC - GF$

   $AD - HG$

   b. The multiplication factor from *ABCD* to *HEFG* is $\frac{8}{20} = \frac{4}{10} = \frac{2}{5}$ or 0.4.

   Check that $\frac{2}{5} \times 20 = \frac{40}{5} = 8$, or $0.4 \times 20 = 8$.

   c. The length of *DC* can be found by calculating $2\frac{1}{2} \times 12 = 30$ or by calculating $12 \div \frac{2}{5} = 30$ or $12 \div 0.4 = 30$.

   d. The pairs of corresponding angles from *ABCD* to *HEFG* are:

   $\angle A - \angle H$

   $\angle B - \angle E$

   $\angle C - \angle F$

   $\angle D - \angle G$

2. **a.** Making a sketch of the two triangles may help in answering this question.

   Corresponding sides are:

   $AB - CD$

   $BC - DE$

   $AC - CE$

   b. Corresponding angles are:

   $\angle A - \angle C$

   $\angle B - \angle D$

   $\angle C - \angle E$

   c. The corresponding angle of $\angle BCA$ is $\angle DEC$.

Hints and Comments

Materials

card stock, optional

Overview

Students investigate other shapes that are similar and learn that in similar shapes, corresponding angles have equal measures.

About the Mathematics

Formal notations are introduced on this page. An angle can be written using a single letter, as in $\angle A$, but also with three letters, $\angle DAB$, describing the "legs" of the angle. The mathematical symbol $\sim$ for similar shapes is also used.

Planning

You may want your students to practice using formal mathematical language by using it yourself when appropriate. For some students, the transition to using more formal mathematical language can prove to be a difficult one. They may need to stay at an informal or preformal level for a longer period of time. Students may work on problems 1 and 2 in small groups or individually.

Comments About the Solutions

2. Usually, when identifying similar triangles, the order of the letters indicates which angles have equal measures and which are the corresponding sides. Since *A* is the first letter in $\triangle ABC$ and *C* is the first letter in $\triangle CDE$, this means that $\angle A = \angle C$. The same argument is used to show that, for example, *AB* and *CD* are corresponding sides in both triangles.

Notes

Make sure students' drawings are accurate before having them measure missing side lengths. Have them mark parallel lines in their drawing.

In your discussion of this activity, you may want to ask students what conclusions they can draw. Summarize these conclusions with the whole class.

Students should use protractors or compass cards to investigate the angle measurements.

Point to Point

On **Student Activity Sheet 3**, side *BC* of △*ABC* has been drawn.

Use a compass to circle a length of exactly 15 cm from point *B* and a length of exactly 12 cm from point *C*.

The intersection point of the two circle parts is point *A*.

Use a ruler or straightedge to complete △*ABC*.

On side *CA*, find point *D* so that *CD* = 4 cm.

On side *BC*, find point *E* so that *DE* is parallel to *AB*.

Copy and fill in the table. Use a centimeter ruler to measure the side lengths you need in whole centimeters.

Corresponding Side Lengths of △*ABC* and △*DEC*			
	ED and *BA*	*DC* and *AC*	*EC* and *BC*
Small Triangle	....	4 cm	....
Large Triangle	15 cm	12 cm	18 cm

What do you notice about the angles of △*ABC* and △*DEC*?

Sandra states in her drawing, ∠ *B* is an obtuse angle. Can Sandra's drawing be right?

Now find point *F* on *BC* so that *DF* = 4 cm. Draw △*DFC*.

Copy and fill in the table. Use a centimeter ruler to measure the side lengths you need in centimeters.

Corresponding Side Lengths of △*ABC* and △*DFC*			
	FD and *BA*	*DC* and *AC*	*FC* and *BC*
Small Triangle	4 cm	4 cm	....
Large Triangle	15 cm	12 cm	18 cm

What do you notice about the angles of △*ABC* and △*DFC*?

Assessment Pyramid

Understand the relationship between parallel lines and equal angles.

Prove that two triangles are similar.

Reaching All Learners

Intervention

Parts of this activity can be modeled on an overhead projector to help those students who have difficulty reading and following directions.

Inform students that they must measure precisely in order to get the same multiplication factor for all three sides.

Solutions and Samples

Activity

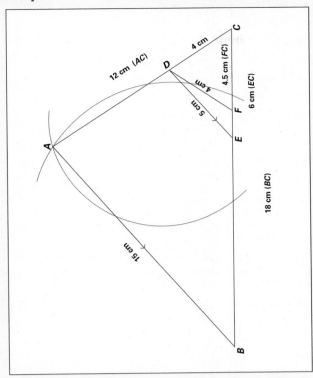

Students should notice that the angles of △ABC and △DEC have equal measures.

Sandra's drawing cannot be correct. The only way ∠B could be an obtuse angle is if the circle drawn from point C is greater than 18 cm (that is, longer than segment BC).

Corresponding Side Lengths of △ABC and △DEC			
	ED and **BA**	**DC** and **AC**	**EC** and **BC**
Small Triangle	5 cm	4 cm	6 cm
Large Triangle	15 cm	12 cm	18 cm

Students should notice that the angles of △ABC and △DFC have no equal measures, except for ∠C which is the same angle in each of the triangles.

Corresponding Side Lengths of △ABC and △DFC			
	FD and **BA**	**DC** and **AC**	**FC** and **BC**
Small Triangle	4 cm	4 cm	4.5 cm
Large Triangle	15 cm	12 cm	18 cm

Hints and Comments

Materials

Student Activity Sheet 3, (one per student); ruler or straightedge, (one per student); compass, (one per student)

Overview

Students make an exact drawing of a triangle from information given in the text. Then two overlapping triangles are created within the large triangle, and students investigate whether these are similar to the large triangle. They observe that similar triangles have equal angle measures. The notion of acute and obtuse angles and their properties is reviewed.

About the Mathematics

This activity is an introduction to the formal rules for similar triangles as expressed on the next page. Students should be able to make an accurate drawing of a triangle, using a compass and straightedge, if the side lengths are given.

Planning

Being aware of measurement imprecision is one thing that comes up naturally here and should be a source for a classroom discussion if you think that is what is needed at that point. Give students a chance to make mistakes and learn from them.

Notes

3c Be sure to discuss students' answers to problem 3c in class. Have a class discussion about the statement in the diagram.

Use the tables from the previous activity to answer the following questions.

3. a. Compare △ABC and △DEC.

Is △ABC ~ △DEC? Give an explanation.

b. Now compare △ABC and △DFC.

Is △ABC ~ △DFC? Give an explanation.

c. What do you think makes triangles similar?

4. a. What is the multiplication factor for △DEC and △ABC?

b. Bill says, "Since *FD* is 4 cm, △ABC can never be similar to △DFC!" Explain whether you agree or disagree with Bill.

In problems 1–4, you investigated when two triangles might be similar. You began with two pairs of corresponding sides having a multiplication factor of 3. The triangles were similar, sides formed parallel lines, and corresponding angles had the same measure.

Then you introduced a third side that had a multiplication factor of 3.75, not 3. The triangles were NOT similar. The corresponding angles did not have the same measure and no sides were parallel.

This chart summarizes what happened.

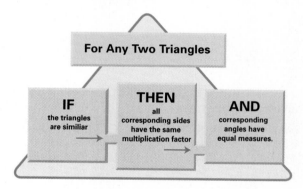

It is important for students to copy the IF-THEN statement into their notebooks and review it frequently.

5. Write the statement in words, using the connectors IF, THEN, and AND.

Reaching All Learners

Accommodation

For students who have difficulty copying tables, prepare a copy of both tables ahead of time so they can concentrate on measuring the side lengths and from page 23 filling in the table, while still keeping up with the rest of the class.

Writing Opportunity

At this point you may want students to summarize their findings about similar shapes and write a few lines about them in their journals.

Solutions and Samples

3. a. $\triangle ABC \sim \triangle DEC$. The table shows that each side length of the small triangle $\triangle DEC$ is multiplied by 3 to find the large triangle $\triangle ABC$. Or: The multiplication factor from triangle $\triangle DEC$ to triangle $\triangle ABC$ is 3. The angles have the same measure.

b. $\triangle ABC$ and $\triangle DFC$ are <u>not</u> similar, so the statement is not true. You can see they are not similar because they do not have the same shape. The sides AB and DF are not parallel. The angles do not have the same measure. Corresponding sides do not have the same multiplication factor as the table shows.

c. Sample answers:
- Corresponding sides have the same multiplication factor.
- The triangles have the same shape.
- Corresponding angles have the same measure.
- You can tessellate the large triangle with the small triangle.

4. a. The multiplication factor from triangle $\triangle DEC$ to triangle $\triangle ABC$ is 3.

b. Sample answer:

I agree with Bill. Since you know that side DC has length 4 cm and $AC = 12$ cm, the multiplication factor for all corresponding sides should be 3. The corresponding side of DF is AB, but the side length of AB is not $3 \times 4 = 12$ but 15.

5. If two triangles are similar, **then** all the corresponding sides have the same multiplication factor, **and** the corresponding angles have equal measures.

Hints and Comments

Materials

copy of tables from page 23, optional

Overview

Students use the results of the Activity on the previous page to determine whether or not triangles are similar.

About the Mathematics

In many of the problems in the previous sections, students were not expected to prove that triangles were similar. Students assumed that triangles were similar and found unknown lengths based on that assumption.

In this section, students learn formal rules about what makes two triangles similar. The relationship between the two statements can be made clear by referring to a tessellation from Section B.

The small triangle fits the same number of times along each side of the large triangle. Thus, the corresponding sides of the small triangle and the large triangle must have the same ratio. It is obvious that the corresponding angles are equal because each angle of the small triangle fits in the corresponding angle of the large triangle.

Planning

You may want to answer the problems on this page as a whole class activity.

Comments About the Solutions

3. c. Students summarize their findings and try to formulate a general rule for similar triangles.

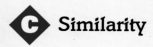
Notes

You will want to make a visual of this chart for your classroom. A copy of a tessellated triangle, such as the one on page 3, helps demonstrate the statement.

The small triangle fits along each side the same number of times; therefore, the corresponding sides all have the same multiplication factor.

Because each small triangle fits in the corresponding angle of the large triangle, the corresponding angles must be congruent.

When you reverse the arrows and switch the connectors, AND and IF, the chart changes into:

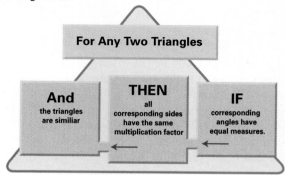

6. Is the statement in the reversed chart also true? Test it with two pairs of triangles and explain your results.

Here are two triangles. One angle is missing from each.

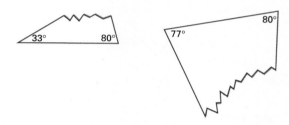

7. If the triangles were completed, would they be similar? Why or why not?

8. Are these right triangles similar? Why or why not?

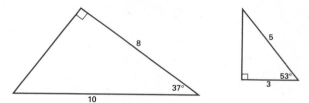

Reaching All Learners

Intervention

If students find it hard to solve the problems on this page, you may need to review the rule that angle measures in a triangle add up to 180°. If students are not sure, ask them to find the size of the third angle. Some students may need extra practice with similar problems.

Solutions and Samples

6. Yes, it is true. Sample triangles:

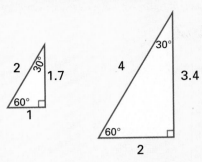

The angles are the same size in both triangles, and the multiplication factor 2 works for all sides.

7. No. Compute the size of the third, torn off angle, in both shapes. Recall that adding the three angles in a triangle results in an angle of 180°.

$80° + 33° + \ldots = 180°$. The size of the missing angle is 67°.

$80° + 77° + \ldots = 180°$. The size of the missing angle is 23°.

There is only one pair of corresponding angles with the same size, so the triangles, if completed are <u>not</u> similar.

8. The triangles are similar. Possible student explanations:

- In the first triangle, the angle sizes are 37°, 53°, and 90° because the angle sizes in a triangle add up to 180°.

  In the second triangle, the angle sizes are 90°, 37°, and 53° for the same reason.

- I used the Pythagorean theorem to calculate the missing side lengths in both triangles:

  $8^2 + ?^2 = 10^2$ $3^2 + ?^2 = 5^2$

  $64 + ?^2 = 100$ $9 + ?^2 = 25$

  $?^2 = 36$ $?^2 = 16$

  $? = 6$ $? = 4$

Then I compared corresponding side lengths in both triangles:

Small Triangle	3	4	5
Large Triangle	6	8	10

The multiplication factor from the small triangle to the large triangle is 2, which means the triangles are similar.

Hints and Comments

Overview

Students check whether the reversed statement of the previous page is also true. They check the rule for similar triangles using the angle measures in a triangle adding up to 180°.

About the Mathematics

There are two ways to prove that two triangles are similar.

- Two triangles are similar if all corresponding sides have the same ratio. In order to draw this conclusion, you have to know the ratios of all corresponding sides.

- Two triangles are similar if all the corresponding angles are equal. To draw this conclusion, it is sufficient to know the measurements of two corresponding angles of each triangle.

Comments About the Solutions

8. Two different strategies are mentioned in the Solutions column. The first one, comparing the angles measures to conclude the triangles are similar. The second one, using the Pythagorean theorem and the multiplication factor is not very efficient but leads to a correct conclusion.
You may want to compare strategies and have students explain which one they would choose themselves and why.

Notes

9 Some students may need to reread the statement on the previous page before doing this problem.

9. Are the following pairs of figures similar? Why or why not?

a

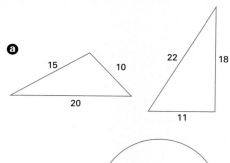

b

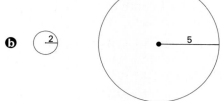

c

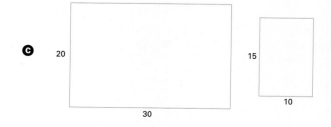

d

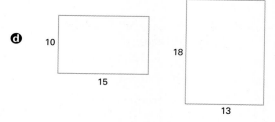

9d A common misconception is addressed in this problem; adding an equal length to both side lengths is not the same as multiplying each side length by the same number.

Assessment Pyramid

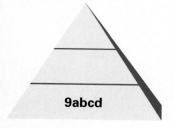

9abcd

Identify similar figures.

Reaching All Learners

Intervention

For problem 9, some students may need coaching on strategies to determine if the multiplication factor or ratio is the same for the corresponding sides. They must first identify the corresponding sides. Then on problems such as 9d, ask them how to find what number times 15 equals 18.

Solutions and Samples

9. Order sides according to length and check for common multiplication factor.

a. Triangles: No.

Small Triangle	10	15	20
Large Triangle	11	18	22

The first and third columns have a common multiplication factor, but not the middle one.

b. Circles: Yes. Note that all circles have the same shape so all circles are similar.

c. Rectangles: Yes.

Small Rectangle	10	15
Large Rectangle	20	30

The multiplication factor is 2.

d. Rectangles: No.

Small Rectangle	10	15
Large Rectangle	13	18

If you add 3 to the lengths of the sides of the small rectangle, you get the lengths of the corresponding sides of the large rectangle. However, to be similar, they need to have the same multiplication factor.

Or: If the side lengths of the large rectangle were 12 and 18, instead of 13 and 18, the rectangles would be similar with a multiplication factor of $\frac{12}{10} = 1\frac{1}{5}$.

$1\frac{1}{5} \times 10 = 12$, and $1\frac{1}{5} \times 15 = 18$.

Hints and Comments

Overview

Students decide whether or not pairs of shapes are similar and why.

About the Mathematics

Students should realize that similar shapes can be shapes other than triangles. For example, all circles are similar, and the multiplication factor can be found by looking at the ratio of the radii. Not all rectangles are similar, even if their angle measures are equal, thus showing students that having equal angle measures is only sufficient for similar triangles.

Planning

Students may work individually or in small groups on problem 9.

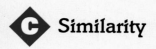
Notes

10a and b Explain that because the sun is so far away, the angle between the sun and the shadow is the same in both triangles at a fixed time of day. We are also assuming that the pole and the tree are perpendicular to the ground.

10b Ask, *Why are the corresponding angles in the two triangles equal?* Sample response: I know that the pole and the tree are both vertical, so they are perpendicular to the ground, which means they are at 90° angles to the ground. The sun will hit both the tree and the pole at the same angle, so I know the angles the sun rays make with the ground are equal.

Shadows

Here is a pole, a tree, and their shadows. The lengths of the pole and both shadows are easy to measure directly, but the tree is too tall to measure directly.

10. **a.** Draw a side view of the pole and its shadow. Consider these as two sides of a triangle. Draw the third side. Draw another triangle representing the tree and its shadow.

   b. Do you need to check that all three pairs of corresponding angles are equal in size before you can conclude that the triangles are similar? Explain your answer.

   c. Suppose you found that the height of the pole is 1.65 m, the shadow of the pole is 2.15 m, and the shadow of the tree is 7.80 m. Find the height of the tree.

Reaching All Learners

Intervention

For problem 10, it may be necessary to review the steps for solving similar triangle problems: Make a sketch. Draw arrows between the corresponding sides. Use a ratio table to solve for the missing length by finding the multiplication factor. Students should record these steps in their notebook.

Extension

Students could find the height of a tree in the school yard or at home by using a dowel rod or meter stick and measuring both of the shadows. Then they solve for the height of the tree, using a ratio table and finding the multiplication factor.

Solutions and Samples

10. a. Drawings will vary. Sample drawings:

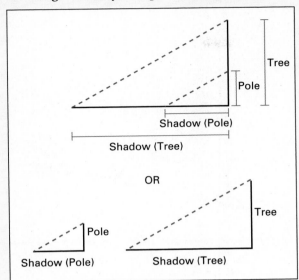

b. No. If two pairs of corresponding angles are equal, then the third pair must also be equal since the sum of the angles in any triangle is 180°.

c. The tree is about 6 meters tall. Strategies will vary. Sample strategy:

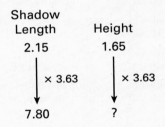

$$1.65 \text{ m} \times 3.63 \approx 6 \text{ m}$$

Hints and Comments

Materials

dowel rod or meter stick, optional

Overview

Students investigate how similar triangles can be used to find the height of a tree. They use the length of a pole and the lengths of the shadows of the tree and the pole.

Planning

Students may work on problem 10 in small groups. When they are finished, you may want to discuss this problem with the whole class.

Comments About the Solutions

10. Students should realize that drawing a side view of a situation is often appropriate. If students have difficulty, you may want to remind them to determine which pairs of angles can be used to prove that the triangles are similar.

a. Students may remember situations with shadows caused by the sun from the unit *Looking at an Angle*. In the same unit, students developed their ability to choose appropriate views to draw situations.

Notes

Takeoff

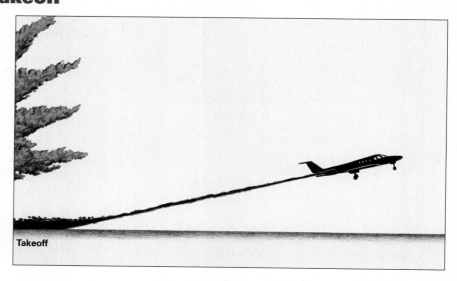

Takeoff

11a Discuss the importance of careful reading to note the phrase "measured along the ground."

11c Students should reread their IF-THEN statement from page 25 if necessary.

11d For some students it is easier to work this problem if they draw the two triangles separately, write the lengths on the sides, draw arrows to the corresponding sides, and then write their ratio table.

11e Explain that answers will vary, depending on how they rounded the multiplication factor.

The drawing represents a plane taking off. At this moment, it is 1,000 m from the point of takeoff, as measured along the ground, and it is 240 m above the ground.

11. **a.** Sketch the situation and label the distances that you know.

 b. On your sketch, extend the plane's takeoff line of flight to a point that is 2,500 m from takeoff (as measured along the ground). Draw in the new height of the plane to the ground, and label your diagram with the new information.

 c. Identify two triangles in your picture. Are they similar? Explain how you know.

 d. When the plane is 2,500 m from the point of takeoff (as measured along the ground), what is its height?

 e. When the plane reaches an altitude of 1,000 m, what is its distance (measured along the ground) from the point of takeoff?

 f. What assumption(s) do you have to make in order to solve **e**? Why is it necessary to make the assumption(s)?

Assessment Pyramid

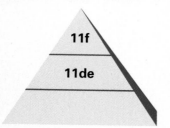

Reason about and use the concepts of ratio, similarity, and properties of similar triangles to solve problems.

Reaching All Learners

Intervention

As students are working on problem 11f, it may be helpful to point out to some students that making a sketch is an important problem-solving strategy, and doing so for 11f will help them think about what they assumed (that the plane continues to climb at the same angle of steepness).

Solutions and Samples

11. a. and **b.**

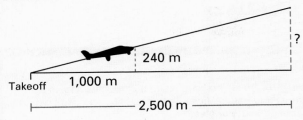

c. Yes, the two triangles are similar. Sample explanation:

These two triangles share the same angle (at takeoff), and they are both right triangles. So the two triangles are similar since they have two pairs of congruent angles.

d. 600 m.

Strategies will vary. Sample strategy:

The multiplication factor for ground distance is 2.5, so the height at a distance of 2,500 meters from takeoff is equal to 2.5 × 240 m, or 600 m.

e. The plane will be about 4,167 meters from the point of takeoff. Sample strategy:

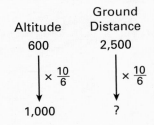

$2,500 \times \frac{10}{6} \approx 4,167$ m

f. You have to assume that the plane continues to climb at the same angle of steepness. It is necessary to assume that the steepness remains the same in order to maintain that the two triangles are similar.

Hints and Comments

Overview

Students examine a plane taking off. They sketch the situation, identify similar triangles, and find the plane's height and distance traveled at various points on its flight path. Students reflect on the assumptions they have to make in order to solve this problem.

Planning

Students may work on problem 11 individually. This problem is critical. Students must visualize the situation, draw a side view, determine the pairs of angles that can be used to prove that the triangles are similar, and then find the unknown length.

Comments About the Solutions

11. a. and **b.**
Students must draw the sides that form the similar triangles.

c. Students have to prove that two triangles are similar.

e. Answers may vary, depending on how students round the multiplication factor. Accept answers between 4,100 m and 4,200 m.

Notes

Students are investigating equal angles and parallel lines, and learning how to use symbols to mark the angles equal in size.

You may wish to have two pairs of angles precut to demonstrate how to overlap the angles.

Have students observe that no matter what size angles they used, parallel sides are always formed.

In both cases, the remaining sides should be parallel. This should occur when angles used to line up the pieces of paper are either obtuse or actue.

Angles and Parallel Lines

Activity

You have worked with several situations that involve angles with equal measures and parallel lines. In this activity, you work with **obtuse angles** and **acute angles**.

Obtuse Angles

- Using plain white paper cut out two obtuse angles that have the same size.

- Position the two angles so that they share one side.

- Glue or tape the angles onto a piece of paper.

- Compare the remaining sides. How would you describe these sides?

Acute Angles

What happens when the angles are acute angles?

Repeat the steps above for two acute angles.

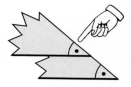 

At the left, two acute angles are marked with black dots. The angles are equal in size, and the dots in the angles indicate the angle measures are equal.

At the right, the two horizontal lines are parallel. The arrows on the lines indicate the lines are parallel.

Reaching All Learners

English Language Learners

Use some kinesthetic examples to review the definitions of *obtuse, acute,* and *right angles,* and *parallel lines,* such as having students demonstrate an obtuse angle with their arms or two pencils. It also helps to have posters in the room with examples of these vocabulary words.

Writing Opportunity

You may ask students to paste the angles they cut out into their notebooks. Then students can add symbols to indicate the equal angles and parallel lines.

Hints and Comments

Overview

Students review the relationship between parallel lines and angles. They draw and cut out two equal obtuse and two acute angles. Then they investigate equal angles and parallel lines. Students review the use of equal symbols to indicate equal angles. There are no problems to solve on this page.

About the Mathematics

The concept of parallel lines intersected by another line and equal corresponding angles formed this way is reviewed. It was addressed earlier, in the unit *Triangles and Beyond*.

Planning

For some students, you may need to recall the difference between an obtuse and an acute angle. Note that equal angles are often indicated by the same symbols. Parallel lines are indicated by one or more arrows.

This activity can be completed quickly with scratch paper. The point is for students to realize that in a situation like this, if the lines are parallel, angles *A* and *B* must be the same, as shown below.

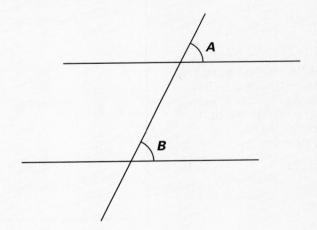

Notes

Providing students with a copy of this page will save time and help those students who have difficulty copying.

When you created the triangle tessellations in Section A, you may have used transformations of the dark triangle to fill up the space.

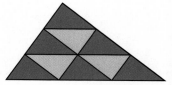

12. Copy the triangles below and mark equal angles with the same symbol.

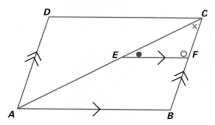

In this diagram, two pairs of parallel lines are marked. Each angle in △*CEF* is marked with a different symbol.

13. Make a copy of the diagram and use these symbols to mark angles with equal measures.

14. a. Name all pairs of similar triangles in this figure. Justify your answers.

   b. Find the lengths of sides *FC, BG, CG,* and *EG.*

14 Remind students that the order of the letters should indicate which angles are congruent. The first letter of each should name equal angles.

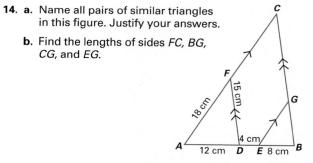

Reaching All Learners

Intervention

Drawing the three triangles separately and writing the lengths on each side is a good way to start problem 14. You might have students make a copy of the drawing in their notebooks and indicate equal angles with the same symbol. Then they draw arrows to the corresponding sides and find the multiplication factor.

Vocabulary Building

Have students include examples for acute, right, and obtuse angles in their notebook.

Solutions and Samples

12.

13.

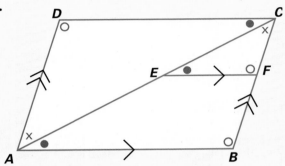

14. a. $\triangle ADF \sim \triangle ABC$

$\triangle EBG \sim \triangle ABC$

$\triangle ADF \sim \triangle EBG$

Explanations will vary. Sample explanations:

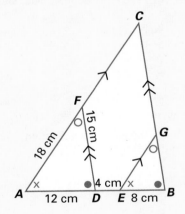

$\triangle ADF$ is similar to $\triangle ABC$. Justification: segment $DF \parallel BC$, so $\angle D = \angle B$, and the triangles have $\angle A$ in common. All corresponding angles are equal in size.

$\triangle EBG$ is similar to $\triangle ABC$. Justification: segment $EG \parallel AC$, so $\angle E = \angle A$, and the triangles have $\angle B$ in common. All corresponding angles are equal in size.

$\triangle ADF$ is similar to $\triangle EBG$. Both triangles $\triangle ADF$ and $\triangle EBG$ are similar to the same $\triangle ABC$, so they are similar to each other.

Hints and Comments

Materials

copy of page 30, optional

Overview

Students identify similar triangles and determine unknown side lengths.

About the Mathematics

The activity on the previous page and the text on this page will help to develop students' ability to recognize corresponding angles and alternate interior angles.

Planning

Students may work on problems 12–14 in small groups or individually.

b. $FC = 18$ cm $BG = 10$ cm

$CG = 20$ cm $EG = 12$ cm

Sample strategy:

Similar Triangles	Side Lengths (in cm)		
ABC	AB = 24	BC = ?	AC = ?
ADF	AD = 12	DF = 15	AF = 18
EBG	EB = 8	BG = ?	EG = ?

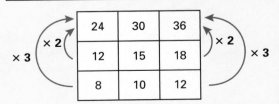

Notes

15 You could have the students predict which triangle will blend perfectly with the trapezoid before they cut out the figures.

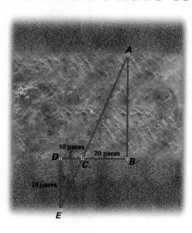

I — 9 cm, 12 cm, 8 cm

II — 10 cm, 12 cm, 8 cm

Trapezoid — 8 cm, 5 cm, 6 cm, 12 cm

15. Cut out the three figures on **Student Activity Sheet 4**. Which triangle, if any, blends perfectly with the trapezoid to form a larger triangle? Explain your answer.

You Don't Have to Get Your Feet Wet

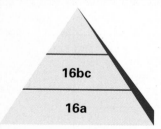

You can use similar triangles to approximate the width of a river. All you would need is four stakes. The diagram is a simplified top view of this situation.

- Start by selecting a place for point *A* on one side of the river. A tree or large rock will work.

- Place a stake at point *B*, directly across the river from point *A*.

- Walk 20 equal paces from *B* parallel to the river to mark point *C*. Then walk another 10 equal paces from *C* to mark point *D*. Place stakes at *C* and *D*.

- From *D*, walk away from the river along a line that is parallel to line *AB*. When points *A* and *C* line up, you are at point *E*. You walked 24 paces from *D* to *E*. Place a stake at *E*.

16. **a.** Name two similar triangles.

   b. Why are the two triangles similar?

   c. Use the triangles in the diagram to find the width of the river.

16 Have students draw a sketch of the triangles in their notebook and label the lengths of the known sides. Discuss different strategies for determining the corresponding angles since one of the triangles is inverted.

Assessment Pyramid

16bc

16a

Use properties of similar triangles to solve problems.

Identify similar figures.

Reaching All Learners

Intervention

For problem 16, students should reread the IF-THEN statement on page 25 if they are not sure of the reason for similarity.

Students should look for parallel lines in order to discover equal angles. They may copy the drawing and indicate equal angles with the same symbol shown in the Solutions column. The angles that are formed are two pairs of alternate interior angles and one pair of vertical angles.

Solutions and Samples

15. Only triangle II can be connected to the trapezoid to form a larger triangle. The ratio of the corresponding sides is the same when triangle II is placed on top of the trapezoid, so a larger triangle can be formed. For triangle I, the ratio of one pair of corresponding sides (9 to 14) is different, so a larger triangle cannot be formed.

16. a. $\triangle EDC \sim \triangle ABC$

b. *AB* and *DE* are parallel, so angles *A* and *E* are equal, and angles *D* and *B* are equal. Finding two pairs of angles that are equal is sufficient to prove that the two triangles are similar.

c. 48 paces (or 96 meters)

The width of the river is 48 paces.
Sample strategy:

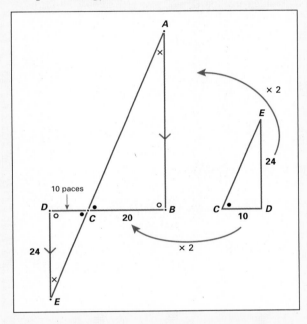

24 × 2 = 48 paces

Hints and Comments

Materials

Student Activity Sheet 4 (one per student)

Overview

Students solve a problem involving similar triangles. They determine the width of a river using the properties of similar triangles.

Planning

Students may work on problems 15 and 16 individually.

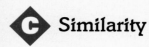

Notes

If you used examples of similar figures to begin this section, students could practice naming those correctly and review the corresponding sides and angles.

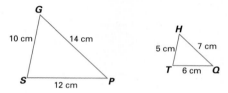

In this section, you explored properties of similar triangles and used triangles to solve problems.

Similar Figures

Two figures are similar if they have identical shapes—not necessarily the same size.

In similar shapes, corresponding angles have equal measures, and the lengths of the corresponding sides have the same multiplication factor.

For example, when △*GPS* is similar *to* △*HQT*, you can write, △*GPS* ~ △*HQT*.

The corresponding angles are ∠*G* and ∠*H*, ∠*P* and ∠*Q*, ∠*S* and ∠*T*.

The corresponding sides are side *GP* and side *HQ*, side *PS* and side *QT*, side *GS* and side *HT*.

The triangles might look like this:

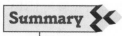

You can use a ratio table to organize information and work with the multiplication factor.

Multiplication Factor: 2	Corresponding Side Lengths of △*GPS* and △*HQT*		
	HT and *GS*	*HQ* and *GP*	*TQ* and *SP*
Small △*HQT*	5	7	6
Large △*GPS*	10	14	12

⤷ × 2

Reaching All Learners

Parent Involvement

You may wish to have students show parents their work from this section and explain how they did the Check Your Work problems.

Hints and Comments

Overview

Students read the Summary, which reviews the main concepts covered in this section.

◆ Similarity

Notes

Discuss with students how important it is to read critically and put the numbers in the correct places in their sketches and in their ratio tables.

Also when they are finished solving for the missing length, they should check to make sure their answer is reasonable. For example, if part of a smaller triangle is missing, the solution must be smaller than the corresponding part of the larger triangle.

2a Some students will benefit from drawing the two similar triangles separately and drawing arrows to the corresponding sides.

The corresponding sides of similar figures are proportional.

You learned that triangles are similar if:

- all pairs of corresponding sides in the two triangles have the same multiplication factor or
- two pairs of corresponding angles have equal measures.

Parallel Lines

Parallel lines produce angles with equal measures.

Here are three parallel lines. The same symbol marks some of the angles with equal measures.

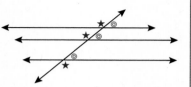

Check Your Work

1. Why is the order of the letters important when you name similar triangles?

Here is an illustration of a swing set.

The two sidebars at each end are 180 cm apart at the ground. The sidebar length from the top to the red crossbar is 88 cm.

The sidebar length from the crossbar to the ground is 128 cm.

2. **a.** Use the information to make a sketch of a triangle at one end of the swing set.

   b. What is the length of the crossbar?

Assessment Pyramid

Assesses Section C Goals

Reaching All Learners

Vocabulary Building

If students are not familiar with the word *proportional*, explain that it means that the corresponding sides have the same multiplication factor or the same ratio.

Extension

Small groups of students could put their work from problems 2 and 3 on an overhead transparency and explain their strategy to the class.

33 It's All the Same

Solutions and Samples

Answers to Check Your Work

1. Here is one reason why the order of the letters is important when naming similar triangles. Your answer might be different from this explanation.

   The order of the letters indicates which sides and angles match up; it sets up the corresponding sides. You don't have to look at the picture to know how the sides and angles are related.

2. **a.** Sample sketch. The drawing does not need to be to scale. Note that making a sketch of the situation first may help you solve the problem.

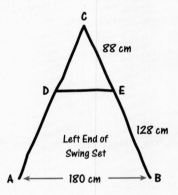

   b. The length of the crossbar is about 73.5 cm. Here is one sample strategy.

   $\triangle ABC$ and $\triangle DEC$ are similar triangles. I assumed the crossbar (DE) is parallel to the ground (AB).

   I found the multiplication factor by dividing 216 by 88 ($216 \div 88 \approx 2.45$). Then I used the multiplication factor in reverse, to find the missing length ($180 \div 2.45 = 73.469$).
   The crossbar will be measured in whole centimeters or at most in half centimeters, so you have to round off the answer to 73 cm or to 73.5 cm.

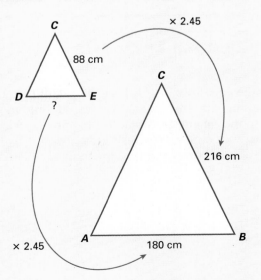

Hints and Comments

Overview

Students read the Summary, which reviews the main concepts covered in this section. Students use the Check Your Work problems as self-assessment. The answers to these problems are also provided on Student Book pages 59 and 60.

Planning

After students complete Section C, you may assign for homework appropriate activities from the Additional Practice section, located on page 54 of the Student Book.

Notes

3b Some students may not realize that if two lines intersect, the opposite angles will always be congruent. Students may need to draw more intersecting lines and check out this relationship.

For Further Reflection

Reflective questions are meant to summarize and discuss important concepts.

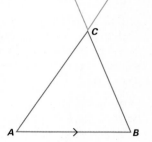

Recall that the arrows in the drawing mean that sides *DE* ∥ *AB,* or side *DE* is parallel to side *AB.*

3. a. What must be true about ∠*CDE* and ∠*ABC*? Why?

    b. What do you know about the other pairs of angles?

    c. Explain why △*ABC* ~ △*EDC.*

    d. If *AC* = 11, *CE* = 4, and *BC* = 7, compute the length of side *CD.*

    e. **Reflect** Is it possible to compute the length of side *AB* with the information you have? Explain why or why not.

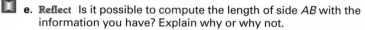

For Further Reflection

In your own words, explain each of these terms. Use drawings to help with your explanations.

- parallel lines
- corresponding sides in similar triangles
- corresponding angles in similar rhombuses
- congruent shapes

Assessment Pyramid

3abcde

▣FFR

Assesses Section C Goals

Reaching All Learners

Intervention

In problem 3d, identifying the corresponding sides is more difficult when one triangle is inverted. Remind students that the corresponding sides are between the pairs of corresponding angles. Angle *B* corresponds to angle *D,* and the two angles at *C* correspond. So *CD* corresponds to *BC.* Also, the longest side of one triangle always corresponds to the longest side of the other triangle.

Vocabulary Building

You may need to review the definition of *rhombus*: a parallelogram with all sides the same length.

Solutions and Samples

3. a. The angles, $\angle CDE$ and $\angle ABC$, have equal measures. When parallel lines are crossed by another line, the alternate interior angles are the same size. This has to be the case; otherwise the lines would not be parallel.

b. The other pairs of alternate interior angles have equal measures. $\angle CED$ and $\angle CAB$ are formed from the parallel lines. $\angle DCE$ and $\angle BCA$ are formed when two lines intersect; the angles across from each other have equal measures.

c. $\triangle ABC \sim \triangle EDC$; the two triangles are similar because two pairs of corresponding angles have equal measures.

d. $CD = 2.5$ cm. Here is one strategy.

$AC = 11$ cm and $CE = 4$ cm. I used these corresponding sides to find that the multiplication factor is $\frac{11}{4}$ (or $2\frac{3}{4}$, or 2.75).

Side CD corresponds to side BC (7 cm). Using the multiplication factor of 2.75, $CD \times 2.75 = 7$ and $CD = 7 \div 2.75$, which is about 2.5.

e. No, it is not possible to compute the length of side AB with the information you have. Though you do know the multiplication factor is $\frac{11}{4}$, you need the length of side DE in order to use the multiplication factor to find the length of side AB.

For Further Reflection

Sample student answers. Note that students may have included drawings by way of explanation.

- parallel lines: lines that show angles with equal measures when intersected by another line that is not parallel; lines that are always the same distance from each other; lines that do not intersect anywhere

- corresponding sides in similar triangles: the matching sides of the two triangles (If you know the length of one of them, you can calculate the length of the other one by using the multiplication factor.)

- corresponding angles in similar rhombuses: the matching angles of the two rhombuses, the angles having equal measures

- congruent shapes: shapes that have the same size and shape; shapes that would totally cover one another if you cut them out and place one on top of the other

Hints and Comments

Overview

Students continue to use the Check Your Work problems as self-assessment. The answers to these problems are also provided in the Student Book, pages 59 and 60.

Planning

After students complete Section C, you may assign for homework appropriate activities from the Additional Practice section, located on page 54 of the Student Book.

Section Focus

In this section, what students learned in previous sections is connected, reviewed, and expanded. Patterns of right triangles within squares are explored, and the areas of similar triangles in these designs are compared. Students apply their knowledge of the properties of similar triangles while solving a variety of realistic problems. They find the width of a porch attached to a house, they investigate special effects for early motion pictures, and decide whether or not a stepladder can be used on the floor space available for it.

Pacing and Planning

Day 11: Patterns		Student pages 35 and 36
INTRODUCTION	Problems 1 and 2	Build a pattern starting with a square and cutting it in half, and use the Pythagorean theorem to find side lengths.
CLASSWORK	Problems 3 and 4	Investigate a halving pattern that starts with a rectangle.
HOMEWORK	Problems 5 and 6	Describe transformations of triangles and find missing angle measures.

Day 12: Using Similar Triangles		Student pages 37–39
INTRODUCTION	Problem 7	Determine whether or not an open stepladder will fit in the space that is available.
CLASSWORK	Problems 8–10	Investigate a pyramid-shaped building using properties of tessellations and similar triangles, and determine the validity of related statements about side lengths and areas
HOMEWORK	Problems 11 and 12	Find the width of a porch and the length of the porch roof using properties of similar triangles.

Day 13: Surface Area by Formula		Student pages 40–44
ACTIVITY	Activity, page 40	Draw the triangles formed by vision lines and a meter stick.
CLASSWORK	Problem 13	Explore triangles formed by the rays of a spotlight, a model, and a shadow.
HOMEWORK	Check Your Work For Further Reflection	Student self-assessment: Use formulas and rules to solve area problems.

Day 14: Summary		Student pages 42-44
INTRODUCTION	Review homework.	Review homework from Day 13.
ASSESSMENT	Quiz 2	Assesses Sections C and D Goals

Additional Resources: Additional Practice, Section D, Student Book page 55.

Materials

Student Resources

Quantities listed are per student.

- **Student Activity Sheet 5**

Teachers Resources

Quantities listed are per pair or group of students.

- Long table (approximately one meter wide)

Student Materials

Quantities listed are per student, unless otherwise noted.

- Blank paper (one sheet per pair of students)
- Centimeter grid paper (two sheets)
- Meter stick (one per pair of students)
- Scissors

* See Hints and Comments for optional materials.

Learning Lines

Characteristics And Properties of Shapes

Students use the Pythagorean theorem to calculate side lengths of a right triangle. They review the classification of triangles and decide which type of triangle, isosceles or equilateral, is used for a tessellation. They use the properties of squares and rectangles to create geometric patterns.

Geometric Relationships

Students use similarity of triangles to solve a variety of problems.

Transformations

Students review transformations as used in tessellations and identify equal angles.

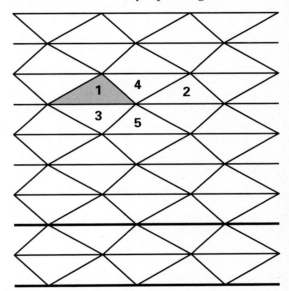

Use Visualization, Spatial Reasoning, and Geometric Modeling to Solve Problems

By using similar triangles, students solve various realistic problems.

At the End of This Section: Learning Outcomes

Students know formal rules to prove whether or not triangles are similar. They can choose their own strategy to solve problems involving similar triangles. They are able to reason mathematically about situations involving similar triangles.

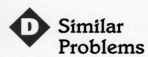
Notes

This section has some Pythagorean theorem problems and problems involving other geometric concepts such as transformations. If it has been awhile since your students used the Pythagorean theorem, you may want to review the theorem before they complete this page.

Similar Problems

Patterns

You can build interesting patterns.

Step 1. Begin with a 2 cm × 2 cm square tile.

Step 2. Make a pattern by dividing the tile into two congruent triangles.

1. What is the length of side *BD*? (Hint: Use the Pythagorean theorem.)

Step 3. Create a strip by repeating the pattern.

Step 4. Repeat the process on the smaller 1 × 1 white square in the bottom left-hand corner.

Each tile now has four small triangles, three white and one red. The smaller triangles are similar to the larger ones.

2. **a.** What are the dimensions of the smaller triangles?

    b. For one tile, what is the total area of the four small triangles?

Reaching All Learners

Extension

Students could explore patchwork quilt designs to see how the patterns were created and how the designs frequently involved similar triangles. Researching how the patchwork quilts were used to help free slaves could be part of an interesting interdisciplinary unit.

Solutions and Samples

1. $BC^2 + CD^2 = BD^2$

$2^2 + 2^2 = BD^2$

$BD^2 = 4 + 4 = 8$

$BD = \sqrt{8} \ (\approx 2.8)$

2. a. $1 \times 1 \times \sqrt{2}$ or $1 \times 1 \times \frac{1}{2}\sqrt{8}$

The multiplication factor from the large triangles to the smaller ones is $\frac{1}{2}$.

The sides of the small right triangle are 1, ($\frac{1}{2} \times 2$).

The hypotenuse is $\frac{1}{2} \times \sqrt{8}$, or about 1.4.

Using the Pythagorean theorem:

The hypotenuse of the small right triangles is $\sqrt{2}$.

$$1^2 + 1^2 = (\text{hypotenuse})^2$$
$$2 = (\text{hypotenuse})^2$$
$$\sqrt{2} = \text{hypotenuse}$$

b. The total area of four small triangles is 2 square units. Sample strategies:

- Four small triangles tessellate the large white triangle. The area of the large white triangle is 2 ($\frac{1}{2} \times 4$), so the area of these four triangles is also 2.

- Use reallotment to find the area of one small triangle. The area of one small triangle is $\frac{1}{4} \times 2 = \frac{1}{2}$. Now multiply by four to find the total area: $4 \times \frac{1}{2} = 2$.

Hints and Comments

Materials

one-cm graph paper (one sheet per student); patchwork quilt designs, optional

Overview

Patterns formed by similar triangles are reviewed and expanded. Students build a pattern starting with a square and cutting it in half by drawing a diagonal. They use the Pythagorean theorem to find side lengths and compare the surface area of similar triangles.

About the Mathematics

In the activity and the problem on this page, a number of mathematical concepts are reviewed and combined: congruent and similar triangles, the use of the Pythagorean theorem, using reallotment to find area measures, and properties of square roots, like $\frac{1}{2}\sqrt{8} = \sqrt{2}$.

Planning

Students may work on problem 2 on their own or in small groups. Discussing results later in class is essential.

Comments About the Solutions

2. Allow students to leave answer $\frac{1}{2} \times \sqrt{8}$ or $\frac{1}{2}\sqrt{8}$. Interesting discussion might occur if other students choose to use the Pythagorean theorem and apparently come up with a *different* answer.

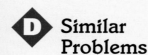

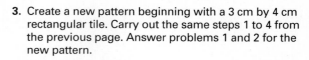

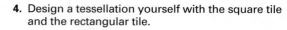

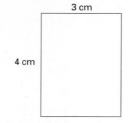

3 cm

4 cm

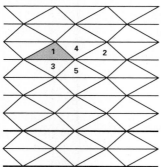

D Similar Problems

Notes

4 It is a good idea to review the exact definition of a *tessellation*: a repeating pattern that uses smaller figures to completely cover a larger figure. There can be no gaps.

6 This problem assumes that students know that the sum of the angles in a triangle is 180 degrees. A nice way to reinforce this is to have them use a triangle made out of paper. Tear off the three angles, then arrange them with the vertices touching to show they form a semicircle or a 180-degree angle.

3. Create a new pattern beginning with a 3 cm by 4 cm rectangular tile. Carry out the same steps 1 to 4 from the previous page. Answer problems 1 and 2 for the new pattern.

4. Design a tessellation yourself with the square tile and the rectangular tile.

All the triangles in the picture are copies of triangle 1. This tessellation used transformations of triangle 1 to create the positions for triangles 2, 3, 4, and 5. Some transformations included rotations, translations or glides, reflections, or flips.

5. Describe each transformation to move triangle 1 into triangles 2, 3, 4, and 5.

Two of the angles in triangle 1 are 42° and 108°.

6. **a.** What is the measure of the third angle of triangle 1?

   b. What are the measures of the angles in triangles 2 and 4? Why?

Using Similar Triangles

Shannon plans to purchase a stepladder so she can reach the top shelf of her closet. The floor space available for opening the ladder is a square, 75 cm × 75 cm.

Reaching All Learners

Act It Out

If any students need practice learning the transformations, show students examples of designs that illustrate *reflection* (flip), *translation* (slide), and *rotation* to help students review these terms. Another good way to reinforce these vocabulary words is to have students do these movements with their bodies: slide to show a translation, turn 180 degrees to show a reflection, and rotate a specific number of degrees about a point for a rotation. Creating a song or chant with movements is also effective.

Solutions and Samples

3. Part I (based on problem 1): The length of the rectangle's diagonal is 5 cm.

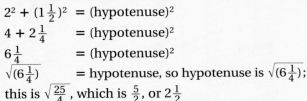

$BC^2 + CD^2 \quad = BD^2$

$3^2 + 4^2 \quad\quad = BD^2$

$9 + 16 \quad\quad = BD^2$

$25 \quad\quad\quad = BD^2$

$\sqrt{25} = BD$, so $BD = 5$

Part II (based on problem 2a): The side lengths of the smaller rectangle
are 1.5 cm, 2 cm, and 2.5 cm.

The multiplication factor from the large triangle to the smaller one is $\frac{1}{2}$.

The legs of the small right triangle are 1.5 and 2, ($\frac{1}{2} \times 3$ and $\frac{1}{2} \times 4$).

The hypotenuse of the small right triangle is $2\frac{1}{2}$, ($\frac{1}{2} \times 5$).

Using the Pythagorean theorem:

$2^2 + (1\frac{1}{2})^2 = (\text{hypotenuse})^2$

$4 + 2\frac{1}{4} \quad = (\text{hypotenuse})^2$

$6\frac{1}{4} \quad\quad = (\text{hypotenuse})^2$

$\sqrt{(6\frac{1}{4})} \quad = \text{hypotenuse, so hypotenuse is } \sqrt{(6\frac{1}{4})}$;
this is $\sqrt{\frac{25}{4}}$, which is $\frac{5}{2}$, or $2\frac{1}{2}$

Part III (based on problem 2b): The total area of the smaller triangles is 6 square cm.

Each triangle has an area $= \frac{1}{2} \times 1.5 \times 2 = 1.5$ sq cm.

The area of one large triangle is half the area of the rectangle.

The area of the rectangle is 12, so half of it is 6.

Four small triangles tessellate one large triangle, so the area of all the small triangles is 6.

4. Designs will vary. Sample designs:

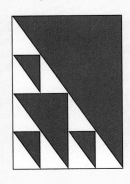 

Hints and Comments

Materials

one-centimeter graph paper (one sheet per student)

Overview

Patterns formed by similar triangles are reviewed and expanded. Students build a pattern starting with a rectangle and cutting it in half by drawing a diagonal. They use the Pythagorean theorem to find side lengths and compare the surface area of similar triangles.

They are introduced to a problem on the facing page: to determine whether or not an open stepladder will fit in the space that is available.

About the Mathematics

Apart from the concepts reviewed on the previous page and repeated on this page, students review the concept of transformations and equal angles.

5.

Triangle Number	Transformation
2	Translation or Glide to right
3	Reflection over horizontal line
4	Rotation and Translation
5	Reflection, Rotation, and Translation, or Reflection and Translation with no Rotation

6. a. 30° (180° − (42° + 108°)). The angle measurements in a triangle add up to 180°.

b. 42°, 108°, and 30°. Since all triangles are copies of triangle 1, the angle measures are equal.

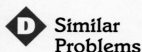
Similar Problems

Notes

7 Discuss with students what strategies they found useful in solving this problem. Students might see that making drawings or that writing in all the known values is critical to the solution. This discussion can review other problems in which drawings or similar strategies were important.

7b Explain that the height is measured on a line perpendicular to the base—like putting two right triangles inside the isosceles triangle. Sketching the right triangle and identifying the lengths of the known leg and hypotenuse are necessary.

At the hardware store, she finds a stepladder that looks like the ones shown here.

She wants to know if the stepladder will fit. The diagram shows the open position for using the ladder.

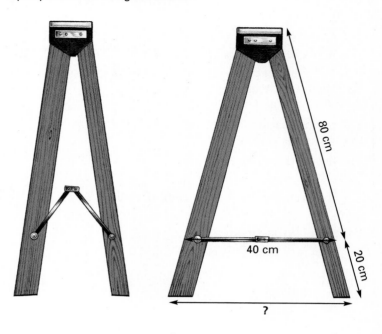

7. a. Will the stepladder fit? How do you know? (Hint: Make a sketch of the ladder and fill in the dimensions you know.)

  b. Use the Pythagorean theorem to compute the height of the ladder in its open position.

  c. What is the height of the ladder in the closed position?

Reaching All Learners

Intervention

For problem 7a, you may need to suggest that students find two similar triangles, sketch them separately, and write in the known lengths of the sides. They then find the multiplication factor to solve for the needed distance.

Extension

Discuss with students how simplifying the ratio of 80 to 100 to solve this problem might be easier than finding the multiplier but that both strategies result in the same solution.

Solutions and Samples

7. a. The ladder will fit; the floor space needed by the ladder in its open position is 50 cm. Student sketches should look similar to this.

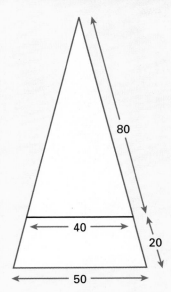

Students may use a variety of strategies to solve this problem. Sample strategy using a ratio table:

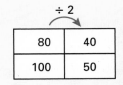

b. The height of the open ladder is about 97 centimeters.

Using the Pythagorean theorem and half the width of 50 cm:

$25^2 + h^2 = (80 + 20)^2$

$625 + h^2 = 10,000$

$\qquad h^2 = 9375$

$\qquad h = \sqrt{9375} \approx 97$

c. 100 cm. The height in the closed position is the hypotenuse.

Hints and Comments

Overview

Students determine whether or not an open stepladder will fit in the space that is available.

Planning

Students may work on problem 7 in small groups. You may want to discuss why the answer is given in whole centimeters and not with one or more decimals.

D Similar Problems

Notes

It is helpful to have a copy of the pyramid cut out before class so you can refer to it during the discussion.

9c Some students may need prompts, such as how long each side of one of the triangles is.
Then find the length of each side of a specific floor, and last find the area.

10 Students should notice that the ratio between the side lengths of the squares is not the same as the ratio between the areas of the squares.

More Triangles

In the pyramid-shaped building pictured here, the faces are made of triangular glass plates. The building has three floors, and the ground floor is a square with side lengths of 30 m.

8. What type of triangle are the glass plates?

9. Use the net for this building on **Student Activity Sheet 5**.

   a. Show where you expect each of the floors to meet the glass plates by drawing floor lines on the net.

   b. Cut out the net. Fold it so the triangles show on the outside.

   c. Find the area of each of the three floors of the building. Explain how you found your answer.

Suppose a floor is halfway between the ground floor and the top of the pyramid. Tell whether each statement is true and explain your answers.

10. a. The new floor is a square.

    b. Each side of the new floor is half the length of a side of the ground floor.

    c. The area of the new floor is half the area of the ground floor.

Reaching All Learners

Intervention

In problem 9c, some students may have difficulty visualizing the shape of each floor. They might be helped by guided questions, such as, *How many sides does each floor have?* and *Is each floor similar to the base?*

Extension

Students may wish to investigate how triangles are used in geodesic domes.

Solutions and Samples

8. Answers will vary. Some students may say that the triangles appear to be equilateral.

9. a. Drawings will vary. Some students may draw a line showing a floor on every other level.

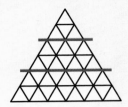

   b. Check students' nets.

   c. Answers will vary, depending on what levels for floors were chosen in problem 9a.

   Sample response:

   The length of a side of each triangle is five meters (30 ÷ 6). If there is a floor on every other level starting from the ground floor, then the areas are as follows:

Area of ground floor:	900 m² (30 × 30)
Area of middle floor:	400 m² (20 × 20)
Area of top floor:	100 m² (10 × 10)

10 a. True. All horizontal floors in this pyramid building are squares.

   b. True. Along the new floor, there are three small triangles, and along the ground floor there are six small triangles, or twice as many as on the new floor.

   Students can also calculate the measurements, 15 meters and 30 meters, and compare them.

   c. False. Sample explanation:

   The area of the new floor is 225 m², (15 × 15). The area of the ground floor is 900 m². Therefore, the area of the new floor is one-fourth, not one-half, the area of the ground floor.

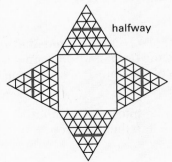

halfway

Hints and Comments

Materials

Student Activity Sheet 5 (one per student); scissors (one pair per student)

Overview

Students investigate a pyramid-shaped building using what they know about tessellation and similar triangles. They use a net of the building for their investigations. Students find measurements of lengths and area.

Planning

Students may work on problems 8–10 individually or in small groups.

Comments About the Solutions

9. Students should recognize each face of the building as a tessellation with the same number of small triangles on each side of the large triangle. This problem should help students to visualize the building. Students may notice that it would not be useful to have a floor at the very top of the pyramid.

Similar Problems

Notes

It is helpful for students to have a copy of this page or have them trace the house and porch. This is a good problem for partners or small groups. Each group could put their strategy on a transparency and then present it to the whole class.

11 If students are having difficulty starting the problem, ask them to look for two similar triangles. Point out that they can draw extra lines in order to form two triangles.

The Porch

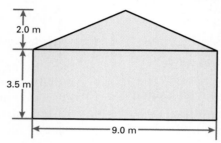

The Koczmericks want to add an enclosed porch to their house.

Here is a side-view sketch of their house.

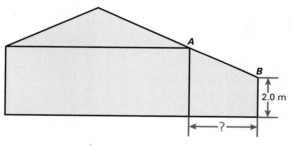

They want the new porch to continue the old roofline until the ceiling height is 2 m.

11. Find the width of the new porch. Explain your answer.

12. The Kozmericks also want to know the length of the porch roof, side *AB*. Compute the length of side *AB*.

Assessment Pyramid

11, 12

Reason about and use the concepts of ratio and similarity in solving problems.

Reaching All Learners

Intervention

If more help is needed in problem 11, ask students where they could draw in two similar right triangles to solve the problem. Some students need to be reminded that the opposite sides of a rectangle are the same length.

Advanced Learners

Ask students who complete problem 12 quickly to use another strategy for finding the length of *AB* and compare it to their first solution.

Solutions and Samples

11. The width of the porch is equal to 3.38 m, or $3\frac{3}{8}$ m. Sample strategy:

The shaded triangles are similar since the base lines are parallel and the corresponding angles are equal.

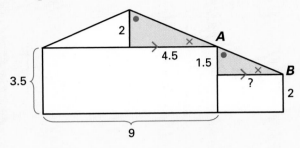

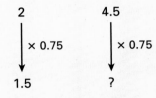

The multiplication factor is 0.75. So the width of the porch is equal to 4.5 × 0.75, which is 3.375 m, rounded to 3.38 m.

12. The length of *AB* is about 3.69 or 3.7 m.

Use the measurements of the shaded right triangle in the new porch (drawing of problem 11) to use the Pythagorean theorem:

$1.5^2 + 3.375^2 = AB^2$

$AB^2 = 2.25 + 11.390625 = 13.640625$

$AB = \sqrt{(13.640625)} \approx 3.69$ or 3.7

Note that if you use calculated measurements in a new problem, you need the real measurements and not rounded off measurements.

Hints and Comments

Overview

Students find the width of a porch and the length of the porch roof that will be added to a house, using the properties of similar triangles.

Planning

Students may work on problems 11 and 12 individually.

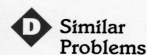

Notes

The activity on this page helps students understand the motion picture problems on the facing page. They will use a piece of paper to block their view of a meter stick and draw the triangle that is formed by the two vision lines and the meter stick.

Explain that the sketch should be a top view of the overlapping triangles formed by the lines of vision and the paper, and the lines of vision and the meter stick. Sketch both the overlapping triangles from the original position and from a position to the left or right.

Hidden Ruler

For this activity, work together with a partner. You need the following materials:

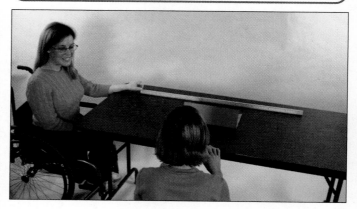

- a long table;
- a meter stick; and
- a rectangular piece of paper.

Place the meter stick and paper as shown in the photo.

- Using one eye, look at the piece of paper. You will notice that the paper hides a portion of the ruler. Have your partner record the length of the hidden portion of the ruler.

- Then move a little to your left or right and tell your partner the length of the hidden portion of the ruler from your new location.

- Change roles with your partner and record two additional measurements.

- Compare the lengths that you and your partner recorded. Explain your observations. Include a sketch that represents each of the four situations.

Reaching All Learners

Extension

Students may wish to repeat the experiment using a piece of paper of a different length or changing the distances.

Writing Opportunity

You may have students write a report about their findings in their journals. Students' reports should include drawings.

Solutions and Samples

Activity

The triangles formed by the lines of sight and the paper are similar to the triangle formed by the lines of sight and the meter stick.

So the length on the meter stick hidden by the paper will always be the same, no matter from what angle you view the meter stick.

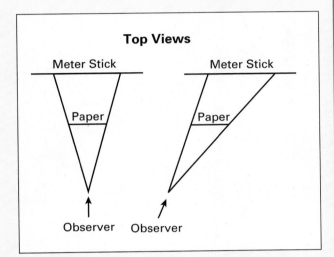

Hints and Comments

Materials

meter sticks (one per pair of students); paper (one sheet per pair of students); long tables (one per pair of students)

Overview

Students carry out an experiment in which they use a piece of paper to block their view of a meter stick, and draw the triangle that is formed by the two vision lines and the meter stick.

About the Mathematics

Students will be working with vision lines and blind spots in the unit *Looking at an Angle*. In that unit, students investigate the ratios of right triangles. In this problem, students deal with different–shaped triangles.

Planning

Students may work on the activity in pairs.

Comments About the Activity

This activity will strengthen students' understanding of angles, similar triangles, and ratios. Make sure students do not think the two large triangles or the two small triangles are similar. Only the large and small overlapping triangles are similar to each other. You may want to challenge students to predict what will happen if the piece of paper is placed farther from the meter stick or where the paper would have to be placed to make the hidden distance 1.5 times the length of the paper.

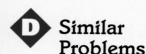

Similar Problems

Notes

Students could try this out by using the light on an overhead projector and making shadows on the screen.

13a Students may need to be reminded that the multiplication factor is between the similar triangles (not 2 to 10). Making a side view drawing of the triangles will help.

13b When using a multiplication factor, some students need to be reminded to check their solution to be sure it is accurate. For example, the height of the model times the multiplication factor should equal 3 meters.

Assessment Pyramid

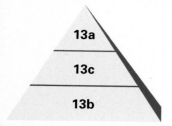

Choose appropriate models and tools, and use properties of similar triangles to solve problems.

Early Motion Pictures

In the early days of movie making, there were no computers to provide animation or special effects. If a script called for a creepy shadow to move along a wall, the director had to be creative. One way they accomplished this effect was to use a small cardboard model of a creepy figure and a spotlight. By placing the small model near the spotlight, a large shadow would appear on the wall.

You may want to use a flashlight and a cardboard model to experiment with these problems.

Here is a diagram of the situation.

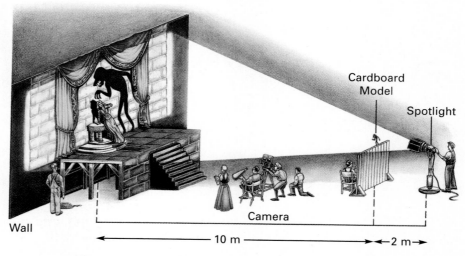

13. **a.** Using the distances in the diagram, find the multiplication factor for the heights of the cardboard model and its shadow.

   b. Suppose the movie director wants the height of the shadow figure to be 3 m. How tall should the model be?

   c. The director does not want the dimensions of the shadow to change as it moves across the wall. Explain how to move the model to satisfy the director.

Reaching All Learners

Intervention

In problem 13c, experimenting with a model first helps students understand how this works. Then review the similar triangles formed as the model moves to the left or right. Referring back to the activity on page 40 will also help.

Solutions and Samples

13. a. The multiplication factor is six.

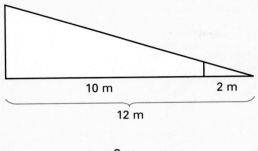

10 m 2 m

12 m

2 m

× 6

12 m

b. The model should be 0.5 m, or 50 cm tall.

?

× 6

3 m

c. The model should be moved along a line parallel to the wall. This can be illustrated with a top-view drawing, as shown below.

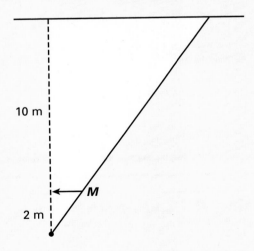

10 m

M

2 m

Hints and Comments

Materials

flashlights, optional (one per student); cardboard, optional (one piece per student); scissors, optional (one pair per student); overhead projector, optional

Overview

Students are introduced to a new context: the use of spotlights to create shadows on a wall. They explore the triangles formed by the rays of a spotlight, a model, and a shadow. Then they explain how to move the model to prevent the dimensions of the shadow from changing as it moves across the wall.

About the Mathematics

The reasoning students use to solve problem 13 is the same as the reasoning they used to do the activity on the previous page of the Student Book.

Planning

You may want to have a class discussion in which you ask students to visualize the situation that is described. You might ask students whether they have ever made shadows on the wall with their hands. Point out that both of these ways of making shadows are based on the same principle. Students may work on problem 13 individually.

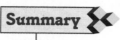
D Similar Problems

Summary

This section showed some interesting problems for using both similar and congruent shapes. You revisited properties of triangles, the Pythagorean theorem, and the usefulness of a multiplication factor.

Check Your Work

Mr. Boyd, the manager of Green's Cafe, wants to advertise his homemade Key lime pie. He decides to place a tripod and a sign in front of the cafe.

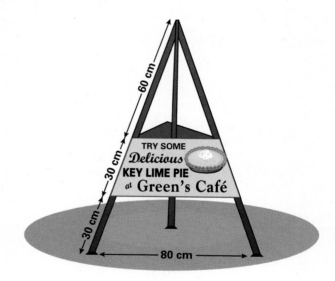

1. Find the horizontal lengths of the sign.

1 Students may solve this by tessellating the larger triangles with the smallest one or drawing three separate triangles, drawing arrows to the corresponding sides, and finding the multiplier.

Assessment Pyramid

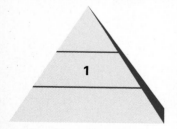

Assesses Section D Goals

Reaching All Learners

Parent Involvement

You may wish to have students show parents their work from this section and explain how they did the Check Your Work problems. You might also challenge students to create their own "similar problems" and share them with parents.

Solutions and Samples

Answers to Check Your Work

1. The top of the sign is 40 cm long, and the bottom of the sign is 60 cm long. Here are two different strategies.

   • Using a drawing and multiplication factors:

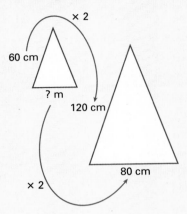

   To find the length of the top of the sign, I used corresponding sides of 60 cm and 120 cm. The multiplication factor is 2. Working in reverse, taking half of 80 cm, the top is 40 cm.

   To find the bottom length, I used corresponding sides of 120 cm and 90 cm. The multiplication factor is 0.75. So 80 cm × 0.75 is 60 cm.

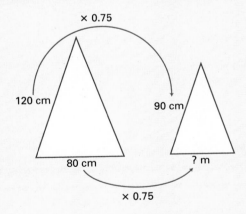

Hints and Comments

Overview

Students read the Summary, which reviews the main concepts covered in this section. They use the Check Your Work problems as self-assessment. The answers to these problems are also provided on Student Book pages 61 and 62.

Planning

After students complete Section D, you may assign for homework appropriate activities from the Additional Practice section, located on page 55 of the Student Book.

   • Using a tessellation:

   A 30 cm by 30 cm by 20 cm will tessellate the large triangle. Two triangles are along the top of the sign (2 × 20 cm) and three triangles along the bottom edge (3 × 20 cm).

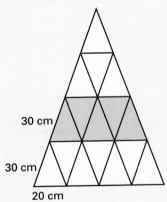

Notes

Students should note that some measurements are in centimeters and some in meters. They may need to review that 100 centimeters equals 1 meter.

Ray uses a box camera to take pictures at a party. He wonders how tall Pauline's image will be inside his camera. Pauline is 1.25 m tall, and she is standing 2.45 m from the camera. The distance between the camera lens and her inverted image is 5 cm.

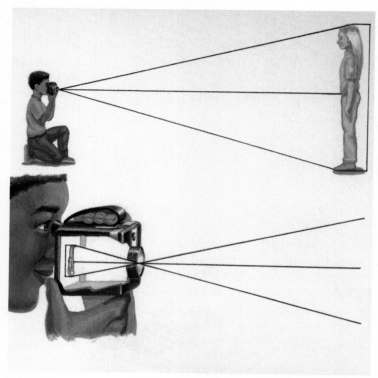

2. How tall is Pauline's inverted image inside the camera?

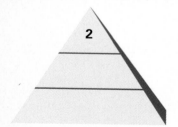

Assessment Pyramid

2

Assesses Section D Goals

Reaching All Learners

Accommodation

Having a meter stick available helps students convert 1.25 meters to 125 centimeters.

Solutions and Samples

2. Paulina's inverted image is 2.6 cm tall. Here is one strategy.

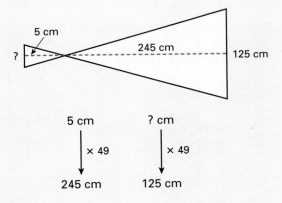

```
    5 cm              ? cm

     │                 │
     │ × 49            │ × 49
     ↓                 ↓

  245 cm            125 cm
```

Hints and Comments

Materials

meter stick, optional

Overview

Students continue to use the Check Your Work problems as self-assessment. The answers to these problems are also provided on Student Book pages 61 and 62.

D **Similar Problems**

One photo shop displays a sign showing possible photo enlargements.

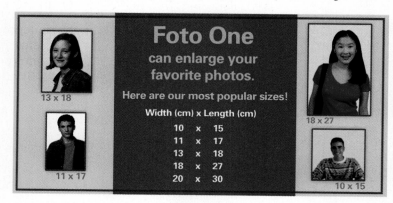

3a When students are finished, you may want to have them share their strategies for showing that the corresponding sides have the same multiplication factor.

3. **a.** Which enlargements are similar in shape?

   b. Wanda places an order for an enlargement to be similar to the 18 × 27 size, with a width of 27 cm. What will the length of her enlargement be?

For Further Reflection

For Further Reflection

Reflective questions are meant to summarize and discuss important concepts.

Painters often paint very high walls and ceilings. To make the job easier, the painters connect two large ladders with a board so they do not have to walk up and down one ladder. They walk across the raised board to paint the higher spots. Suppose each ladder has the same number of steps. The painter puts a board resting on the third step on either side. If the ladder is standing on horizontal ground, will the board be horizontal? Explain.

Assessment Pyramid

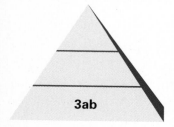

3ab

Assesses Section D Goals

Reaching All Learners

Accommodation

If students have difficulty getting started on the For Further Reflection problem, it may help to have them use a meter stick as a model for the board and a couple of chairs to represent the steps on the ladder. Then investigate when the board would be horizontal and when it would not be.

Extension

You may want to have students investigate the *golden ratio* and share this information with the class.

Solutions and Samples

3. a. 10 × 15, 18 × 27 and 20 × 30 are similar sizes.
Here is a strategy using a ratio table.

×2   ÷10

Width of Photo	10	20	2	18	**12**	11	27
Length of Photo	15	30	3	27	18	**16.5**	40.5

⟩ × 1.5

Sizes 13 × 18 and 11 × 17 do not fit into this ratio table. These are the sizes that are *not* similar to the other sizes.

b. Extending the ratio table above to a width of 27 cm, produces a length of 40.5 cm.
The enlargement is similar to 18 × 27; when the width is 27, the length should be 40.5 cm.

For Further Reflection

The board will be horizontal. Sample explanation:

The board is horizontal because the triangles formed by the ladder and the ground and the ladder and the board are similar. Each ladder has the same number of steps. In the example shown, on one side they are 27 cm apart, and on the other side they are 21 cm apart. Each side of the ladder in the example has 9 steps. The multiplication factor would be 1.5.

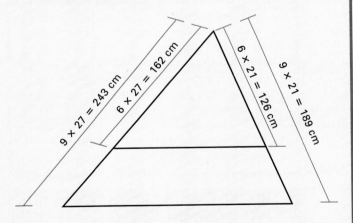

Small Triangle	162 cm	126cm
Large Triangle	243 cm	189cm

⟩ × 1.5

Hints and Comments

Overview

Students continue to use the Check Your Work problems as self-assessment. The answers to these problems are also provided on Student Book pages 61 and 62.

Section Focus

In this section, the contents of the previous sections as well as the contents of previous units are now formalized. The concepts of parallel and perpendicular lines are used to introduce students to formal mathematical reasoning and proof. The concept of slope was addressed earlier in the algebra units and was formalized in *Graphing Equations*. Students practice finding the slopes of lines drawn in a coordinate system. They use coordinate geometry to represent and examine the properties of geometric shapes. They prove that a rhombus has equal side lengths and that the diagonals of a rhombus are perpendicular to each other. The Pythagorean theorem is used to calculate the distance between two points in a coordinate system. The distance formula, based on the theorem as well, is not used here.

Pacing and Planning

Day 15: Parallel and Perpendicular		Student pages 45 and 46
INTRODUCTION	Problem 1	Draw triangles in a coordinate system and use the concepts of slope and parallel lines to prove whether or not triangles are similar.
CLASSWORK	Problems 2 and 4	Use coordinate geometry to review the properties of a parallelogram.
HOMEWORK	Problem 3	Find the slope of various lines.

Day 16: Parallel and Perpendicular (Continued)		Student pages 47–49
INTRODUCTION	Problems 5 and 6	Investigate the concept of perpendicular lines while solving problems that involve similar right triangles.
CLASSWORK	Problems 7 and 8	Solve problems involving the design of roads that are perpendicular or parallel to each other.
HOMEWORK	Problem 9	Use mathematical proof to show a quadrilateral is a rhombus.

Day 17: Length and Distance (Continued)		Student pages 49–51
INTRODUCTION	Review homework.	Review homework from Day 16.
CLASSWORK	Problems 10 and 11	Use mathematical proof to show that the diagonals of a rhombus are perpendicular to each other.
ASSESSMENT	Check Your Work For Further Reflection	Student self-assessment: Use formulas and rules to solve area problems.

Additional Resources: Additional Practice, Section E, Student Book page 56

Materials

Student Resources

Quantities listed are per student.

- **Student Activity Sheet 6**

Teachers Resources

No resources required

Student Materials

Quantities listed are per student.

- Graph paper (three sheets)
- Scissors

* See Hints and Comments for optional materials

Learning Lines

Characteristics and Properties of Shapes

Students recall that parallel lines have equal slopes, and they now learn that if lines are perpendicular, their slopes have the opposite sign and are reciprocal numbers.

Students learn (and prove) that a rhombus has equal side lengths and the diagonals of a rhombus are perpendicular. They use their own strategy to show a triangle has a right angle. They learn the properties of a kite (two pairs of equal sides, diagonals are perpendicular).

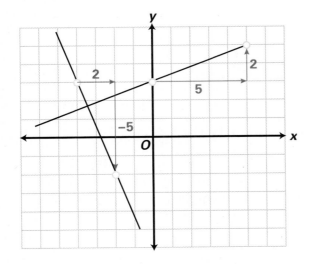

Geometric Relationships

Students use the Pythagorean theorem to calculate the distance between two points in a coordinate system.
For example, in this diagram, $PQ^2 = RQ^2 + RP^2$.

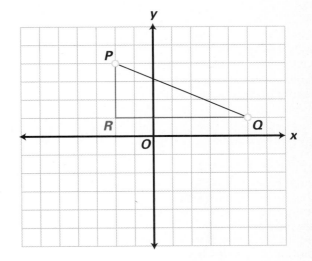

Use Visualization, Spatial Reasoning, and Geometric Modeling to Solve Problems

Students use similar triangles to solve problems within the context of coordinate geometry.

At the End of This Section: Learning Outcomes

Students have used the Pythagorean theorem and its inverse. They can use the theorem to calculate the distance between two points in a coordinate system. They are introduced to more formal mathematical reasoning and proof within the context of coordinate geometry. For example, they can prove whether or not a quadrilateral is a rectangle, a rhombus, or a parallelogram.

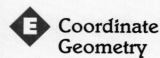

 Coordinate Geometry

Notes

This section investigates the slopes of parallel and perpendicular lines. Many of the problems require students to create a coordinate grid on graph paper. If time is a concern, you may want to have coordinate graph paper available for your students, especially for those who require extra time to create a coordinate grid.

1b Lines *AC* and *DF* are close to being parallel, so students may need to extend these lines to realize that they are parallel. Be sure to discuss different solution strategies used by students.

2 If students have difficulty, remind them of parallel lines having equal slopes.

Coordinate Geometry

Parallel and Perpendicular

In the unit *Graphing Equations*, you learned about parallel lines in a coordinate system. Parallel lines have the same steepness, or **slope**, provided that coordinate axes are scaled in the same way. Recall:

$$\text{slope} = \frac{\text{vertical distance}}{\text{horizontal distance}}$$

1. a. Use graph paper to set up a coordinate system so the *x*-axis and the *y*-axis both have numbers in the range from −10 to 10. Plot the points *A*(−5, −5); *B*(5, −5); and *C*(5, 10). Connect the points to make △*ABC*. Do the same for the points *D*(−4, 2); *E*(−2, 2); *F*(−2, 5) and △DEF.

b. Are sides *AC* and *DF* parallel?

c. Is △*ABC* ~ △*DEF*? Why or why not?

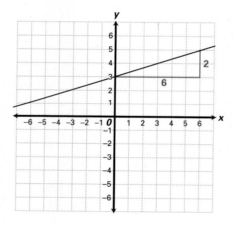

In this coordinate system, the slope of the line through (0, 3) and (6, 5) is $\frac{2}{6}$ or $\frac{1}{3}$.

2 a. Use graph paper to set up this coordinate system. Draw a line through (2, 2) and (6, 3).

b. Is the line parallel to the line through (0, 3) and (6, 5)?

c. What is the slope of the new line?

d. Copy and complete the statement: The line through (2, 2) and (**?**, 3) is parallel to the line through (0, 3) and (6, 5) because its slope is $\frac{1}{3}$.

Reaching All Learners

Intervention

For problem 2d, rolling a piece of spaghetti parallel to the line through (0, 3) and (6, 5) is a strategy that some may need. Looking at fractions equivalent to $\frac{1}{3}$ may help others.

Solutions and Samples

1. a. Sample coordinate system:

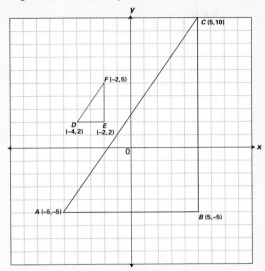

b. The segments *AC* and *DF* are parallel.

Sample explanation:

From *A* to *C*, you move 10 units to the right and 15 units up. This is a ratio of 10:15, or 2:3.

From *D* to *F*, you move two unit to the right and three units up. This is also a ratio of 2:3. So the segments are parallel.

c. The triangles △*ABC* and △*DEF* are similar. Sample explanation:

Both triangles are right triangles with right angles at *B* and *E*. Since *AC* and *DF* are parallel, the other pairs of corresponding angles are equal.

2. a.

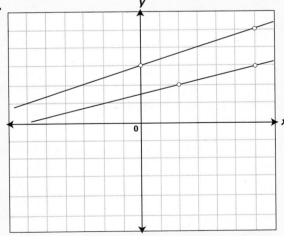

Hints and Comments

Materials

graph paper (one sheet per student); dry spaghetti, optional

Overview

Students draw triangles in a coordinate system and use the concepts of slope and parallel lines to prove whether or not triangles are similar.

About the Mathematics

In this section, the concepts of parallel and perpendicular lines are used to introduce students to more formal mathematical reasoning and proof. The concept of slope is introduced in the unit *Graphing Equations*. Parallel lines have equal slopes.

Planning

If students need more practice to recall the concept of slope, use pages 59–65 of the *Algebra Tools* resource. On this page students start with a problem that involves triangles that are similar. You may want to start this section by working on this problem as a whole class activity.

b. The line through (2, 2) and (6, 3) is not parallel to the original line.

c. The slope of the line through (2, 2) and (6, 3) is $\frac{1}{4}$.

d. The line through (2, 2) and (5, 3) is parallel to the line through (0, 3) and (6, 5) because its slope is $\frac{1}{3}$.

E Coordinate Geometry

Notes

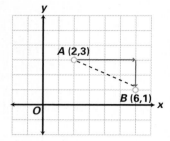

A (2,3)

B (6,1)

O

It is common to read a graph from left to right, just the same as you read text in a book. For this reason, you can say the lines you drew in the previous problem *go up*. Their slope is a positive number. If a line *goes down,* it makes sense that the slope is a negative number.

The slope of the line through *A*(2, 3) and *B*(6, 1) is $\frac{-2}{4}$, or $-\frac{1}{2}$.

3 Remind students to use whole number distances when finding the horizontal change and the vertical change. For these lines, the endpoints could be used to draw the right triangles for counting the horizontal and vertical change. Some students find it easier if they have a copy so they can actually draw the right triangles and then count the lengths.

3. Find the slope of each line.

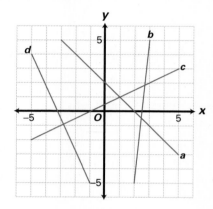

4. **a.** In your own coordinate system, plot the points *A*(4, 2), *B*(9, 5), and *C*(10, 9). Connect point *A* to point *B* and point *B* to point *C*.

   b. What is the slope of the line through *A* and *B*? Of the line through *B* and *C*?

   c. Find the coordinates of point *D* so that quadrilateral *ABCD* is a parallelogram.

   d. How can you be sure quadrilateral *ABCD* is a parallelogram?

Assessment Pyramid

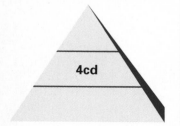

4cd

Understand the relationship between parallel lines, equal angles, and slope.

Reaching All Learners

Intervention

A common mistake with problem 3 is for students to forget the negative sign on the slope. Advise them to find the sign first and then find the fraction for the slope.

Solutions and Samples

3. line labeled: slope

a $\frac{-3}{3} = -1$

b $\frac{10}{1} = 10$

c $\frac{2}{4} = \frac{1}{2}$

d $-\frac{9}{4}$ or $-\frac{9}{4}$

4. a.–c.

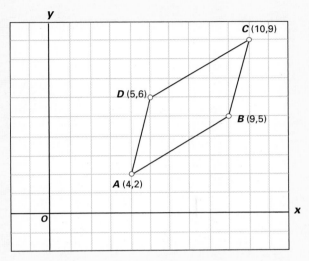

b. slope of line segment AB: $\frac{3}{5}$

slope of line segment BC: $\frac{4}{1} = 4$

c. coordinates D (5, 6)

d. slope of line segment AD: $\frac{4}{1} = 4$

AD and BC have the same slope, so $AD \parallel BC$

slope of line segment DC: $\frac{3}{5}$

AB and DC have the same slope, so $AB \parallel DC$.

The quadrilateral $ABCD$ consists of two pairs of parallel lines, which means $ABCD$ is a parallelogram.

Hints and Comments

Overview

Students find the slope of straight lines. They use coordinate geometry to review the properties of a parallelogram.

About the Mathematics

For some students it is not obvious at all that graphs are read from left to right. A quadrilateral is a parallelogram if it consists of two pairs of parallel lines.

Planning

If students need more practice to recall the concept of slope, use pages 59–65 from the *Algebra Tools* resource. Students may work on the problems on this page individually or in small groups. Problem 3 may be assigned as homework. For some students, you may need to review the properties of a parallelogram after they finish problem 4.

Comments About the Solutions

4. More formal mathematical reasoning is required for problem 4d.

Notes

If students are not sure how to make a mathematical argument, suggest they reread the IF–THEN statement for proving similarity from page 25, either proving the corresponding sides have the same multiplication factor or all corresponding angles are congruent.

5b You may need to ask students how they can determine the corresponding sides when the orientation is different for each triangle.
One strategy is the shortest side corresponds to the shortest side of the larger triangle, and the longest side corresponds to the longest side of the larger triangle.

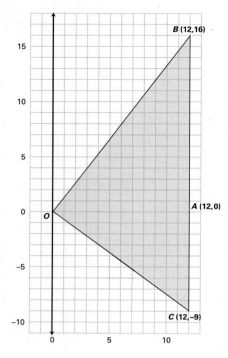

Consider the triangles in this drawing.

5 a. Martin claims that $\triangle OAB$ and $\triangle CAO$ are similar triangles. Use a mathematical argument to support Martin's claim.

   b. The large triangle, $\triangle COB$, is similar to both $\triangle OAB$ and $\triangle CAO$. Prove this statement is true.

   c. What does the statement from problem **b** imply for the size of $\angle BOC$?

Now you know $\triangle COB$ has a right angle at $\angle O$. This means that side OB and side OC are **perpendicular**. A short notation for two sides that are perpendicular is sides $OB \perp OC$.

6. a. Use the drawing from problem 5 to show that the slope of the line through O and B is $\frac{4}{3}$.

   b. Also show that the slope of the line through O and C is $-\frac{3}{4}$. Show your work.

   c. What do you notice about the slopes of sides OB and OC?

Sides that are perpendicular have slopes that are opposite and reciprocal numbers.

7 a. Use graph paper to set up your own coordinate system. Draw any line with slope $\frac{1}{3}$ and an intersecting line with slope -3.

   b. Explain why the two lines must be perpendicular.

   c. If another line has slope 2, what is the slope of a line perpendicular to this one?

Assessment Pyramid

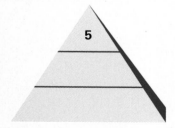

Choose tools to solve geometrical problems involving similar triangles.

Reaching All Learners

Vocabulary Building

Reciprocal may be a new term for students. Explain that two fractions are reciprocals if their product is 1. For example, the reciprocal of $\frac{2}{3}$ is $\frac{3}{2}$, and the reciprocal of 3 is $\frac{1}{3}$. The term *perpendicular* also may need to be reviewed. Students could look for examples of perpendicular lines in the classroom—lines that meet to form all right angles.

Writing Opportunity

You may want your students to write statements about parallel and perpendicular lines in their journals. They should include drawings to support their statements.

Solutions and Samples

5. a. $\triangle OAB \sim \triangle CAO$. Sample arguments:

Use the Pythagorean theorem to compute the side length of the hypotenuse in both triangles:

$9^2 + 12^2 = OC^2 \qquad\qquad 12^2 + 16^2 = OB^2$

$81 + 144 = OC^2 \qquad\qquad 144 + 256 = OB^2$

$OC^2 = 225 \qquad\qquad\qquad OB^2 = 400$

$OC = 15 \qquad\qquad\qquad\quad OB = 20$

Now look at the side lengths of corresponding sides of both triangles.

$\triangle OAB$	OA = 12	AB = 16	OB = 20
$\triangle OAB$	CA = 9	OA = 12	OC = 15

From the table, you can conclude that the multiplication factor from $\triangle CAO$ to $\triangle OAB$ is $1\frac{1}{3}$.

b. Compare the side lengths of $\triangle COB$ to the corresponding side lengths of $\triangle OAB$.

$\triangle COB$	CO = 15	OB = 20	BC = 25
$\triangle OAB$	OA = 12	AB = 16	OB = 20

From the table, you can conclude that the multiplication factor from $\triangle OAB$ to $\triangle COB$ is $1\frac{1}{4}$. Since $\triangle OAB \sim \triangle CAO$, there is no need to prove that $\triangle COB \sim \triangle CAO$.

c. $\angle BOC$ is equal in size compared to $\angle OAC$ and $\angle OAB$. Since the last two angles are 90°, you may conclude $\angle BOC$ is a right angle.

6. a. Slope is $\frac{16}{12}$, which is equal to $\frac{4}{3}$.

b. Slope is $\frac{-9}{12}$, which is equal to $-\frac{3}{4}$.

c. If you compare the slope of the two lines, you see the numbers are each other's opposite and reciprocal.

7. a. Student answers may vary. Sample drawing:

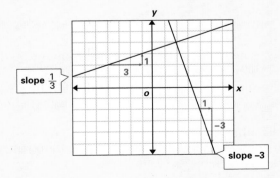

b. The numbers -3 and $\frac{1}{3}$ are each other's opposite and reverse.

c. Slope is $-\frac{1}{2}$. Note that 2 can be written as $\frac{2}{1}$.

Hints and Comments

Materials

graph paper (one sheet per student)

Overview

Students are introduced to the concept of *perpendicular lines* while solving problems that involve similar right triangles.

About the Mathematics

Straight lines that are perpendicular have slopes that are opposite and reciprocal numbers, such as $\frac{3}{4}$ and $-\frac{4}{3}$.

There are different ways to prove a triangle has a right angle:

- Use the reverse of the Pythagorean theorem: If sum of the squares of two sides equals the square of the third side, the triangle is a right triangle.
- Use the slope of two sides and prove these are opposite and reciprocal numbers.
- Use the (given) angle measures of two angles to show they add up to 90°.

Planning

Problem 5 introduces students to the concept of perpendicular lines and their slope. You may want students to solve problem 5 individually first and discuss the results in class before they continue with problems 6 and 7. Encourage students to use formal mathematical arguments to support their views.

Comments About the Solutions

6. This problem is critical for students' understanding of the concept of perpendicular lines.

Coordinate Geometry

Notes

Roads to Be Crossed

Roads are the safest and offer the best view to drivers and pedestrians when the roads intersect at an angle of 90°. Here is the map of an area where a new road will be built.

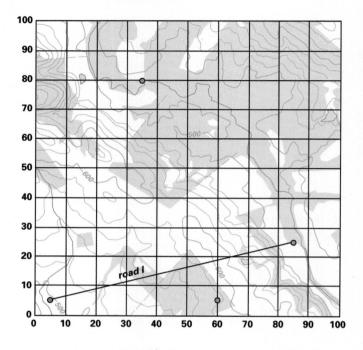

Road I goes through coordinates (5, 5) and (85, 25). An engineer proposes to build the new road II through (35, 80) and (60, 5). Use **Student Activity Sheet 6** to answer question 8.

8. **a.** Is this new road II perpendicular to road I?

   b. Road II needs to go through (35, 80) and be perpendicular to road I. What would you propose if you were the engineer designing the new road?

   c. Draw a road III through (40, 50) that is parallel to road I. How can you be sure this road is parallel to road I?

8 If students are not sure how to begin, ask them what we know about the slopes if the lines are perpendicular. Then have them find the slope of road I and road II.

Assessment Pyramid

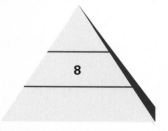

8

Understand the relationship between parallel lines, perpendicular lines, and slope.

Reaching All Learners

Intervention

Some students have difficulty remembering the order of the numbers in the ratio for the slope. It helps for them to know that a slope of 1 means a 45 degree angle with the horizontal and a reasonable estimate for the angle formed by a line with a slope of $\frac{1}{4}$ as opposed to a slope of 4. Having students model a slope of positive 1 with a pencil or ruler at the appropriate angle, then model other slopes, such as 4 or $\frac{1}{4}$, could be used as a warm-up activity before doing the problems on this page. Contrasting positive and negative slopes could also be part of this warm-up activity.

Solutions and Samples

8. a. The new road II is not perpendicular to road I. Sample explanation:

The slope of road I is $\frac{20}{80}$ or $\frac{10}{40}$ or $\frac{1}{4}$.

The slope of road II is $\frac{-75}{25} = -3$. This is not the opposite and reciprocal of $\frac{1}{4}$.

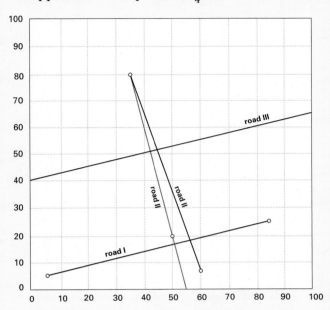

b. I would propose to build the road through (35, 80) and (50, 20) as shown in the drawing. The slope of this road is $\frac{-60}{15}$ or -4. This is the opposite and reciprocal of $\frac{1}{4}$, so the roads are now perpendicular.

c. You can be sure that road III is parallel to road I if both have the same slope, that is $\frac{20}{80}$ or $\frac{10}{40}$ or $\frac{1}{4}$.

Hints and Comments

Materials

Student Activity Sheet 6 (one per student); scissors (one pair per student)

Overview

Students solve problems involving the design of roads that are perpendicular or parallel to each other.

Planning

You may want to introduce this problem by having a classroom discussion about roads in your own community. Why are roads safer if they are perpendicular?

Comments About the Solutions

8. This problem requires formal mathematical reasoning.

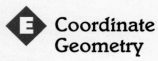
Notes

Length and Distance

In this coordinate system, part of rhombus *ABCD* is drawn.

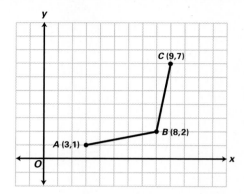

9 Be sure students know that a rhombus has all sides of equal length before they do this problem.

9. a. Use graph paper to copy this drawing. Complete the rhombus by drawing the missing point *D*. What are the coordinates of point *D*?

b. Check that sides *AB* and *CD* are parallel. Answer the same question for sides *AD* and *BC*.

c. In a rhombus, all sides have equal lengths. How can you be sure quadrilateral *ABCD* is a rhombus? Show your work.

10 Some students may need to brainstorm ideas for finding the length because they may not see that they could draw in a right triangle and use the Pythagorean theorem. If necessary, ask if they can find a right triangle so they can use the Pythagorean theorem.

The length of segment *AB* is also referred to as the **distance** between the points *A* and *B*. Side *AB* is also referred to as **line segment** *AB*.

10. Find the distance between the points *A* and *C* in the drawing of problem 9.

The line segment *AC* is a **diagonal** of the rhombus *ABCD* from problem 9.

11. a. Draw the other diagonal of rhombus *ABCD*.

b. Is the distance from *A* to *C* equal to the distance from *B* to *D*?

c. Prove that the diagonals of the rhombus *ABCD* are perpendicular.

10 Discuss with students why sometimes an exact answer, like $\sqrt{72}$ (or $6\sqrt{2}$), is more appropriate and sometimes an estimate, like 8.5, is needed.

Assessment Pyramid

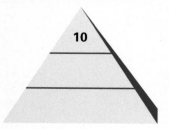

Choose appropriate models and tools to solve geometric problems.

Reaching All Learners

Intervention

Before having students work on this page, you may want to review the essential ideas: parallel lines have the same slope, perpendicular lines have slopes that are the opposite and reciprocal, and the Pythagorean theorem can be used to find the distance between two points.

Extension

After completing problem 11c, students could check to see if the diagonals are perpendicular in a parallelogram that is not a rhombus.

Vocabulary Building

Have students include definitions and examples for distance, line segment, and diagonal in their notebooks.

Solutions and Samples

9. a.

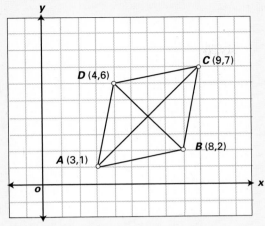

The coordinates of the missing vertex are D (4, 6).

b. Slope of AB is $\frac{1}{5}$; slope of CD is $\frac{1}{5}$; $AB \parallel CD$.

Slope of AD is $\frac{5}{1}$ or 5; slope of BC is $\frac{5}{1}$ or 5; $AD \parallel BC$.

c. Some students may argue you can use the Pythagorean theorem to show that all side lengths of $ABCD$ can be found by calculating $\sqrt{5^2+1}^2$. Other students may point out that all sides are the diagonal of a 5-by-1 rectangle.

10. The distance between the points A and $C \approx 8.5$. Sample explanation:

$AC^2 = 6^2 + 6^2$

$AC^2 = 36 + 36 = 72$

$AC = \sqrt{72} \approx 8.5$

11. a. See drawing for problem 9a.

b. The distance from A to C is not equal to the distance from B to D.

$AC^2 = 6^2 + 6^2 = 72$

$BD^2 = 4^2 + 4^2 = 32$

c. Slope of AC is $\frac{6}{6}$ or 1;

slope of BD is $\frac{4}{4}$ or -1;

so $AC \perp BD$.

Hints and Comments

Materials

graph paper (one sheet per student)

Overview

Students use formal mathematical proof to show a quadrilateral is a rhombus and that the diagonals of a rhombus are perpendicular to each other. They are introduced to the concept of distance between two points in a coordinate system.

About the Mathematics

The distance between two points in a coordinate system is defined as the length of the line segment that joins both points. The length of this segment is calculated with the use of the Pythagorean theorem, but no formula is given yet.

The concepts learned in this section are used to formally prove why a quadrilateral is a rhombus with diagonals that are perpendicular. Students will, of course, encounter more formal proofs during their future education.

Planning

You may want your students to work individually or in small groups on the problems on this page and discuss student work afterward in class. You may want to check students' answers to problem 9a before continuing with the rest of the problems.

Extension

Have students make a drawing of a rectangle in a coordinate system. Let them prove opposite sides are equal in length as well as parallel and that the diagonals of a rectangle are equal in length.

Coordinate Geometry

Notes

A strategy for processing the Summary is to have groups of students make posters for each of the three important points: parallel lines have the same slope, perpendicular lines have slopes that are the opposite reciprocals, and the Pythagorean theorem can be used to find the distance between two points.

Summary

If two lines are parallel, they have the same slope.

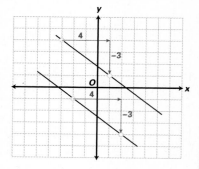

If two lines are perpendicular, their slopes have the opposite sign and are reciprocal numbers.

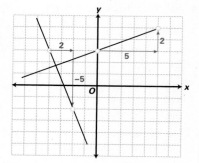

The distance between two points P and Q in a coordinate system is the same as the length of the line segment PQ. You can use the Pythagorean theorem to find the distance between two points in a coordinate system.

$$PQ^2 = RQ^2 + RP^2$$

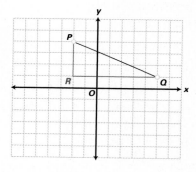

Reaching All Learners

Act It Out

Kinesthetic movements can be used to reinforce the vocabulary words *parallel* and *perpendicular* and what is true about the slopes of those lines. For example, students could model parallel and perpendicular lines with their arms or with pencils and then explain what they know about the slopes.

Hints and Comments

Overview

Students read the Summary, which reviews the main concepts covered in this section.

For Further Reflection

Reflective questions are meant to summarize and discuss important concepts.

Check Your Work

1. **a.** A straight line has slope $\frac{2}{3}$. What is the slope of a line that is perpendicular to this line?

   b. A straight line has slope $\frac{2}{3}$. What is the slope of a line that is parallel to this line?

2. **a.** In your own coordinate system, plot the points $O(0,0)$, $A(6,2)$, $B(5,5)$, and $C(2,6)$. Connect the points to make quadrilateral $OABC$.

   b. Quadrilateral $OABC$ is called a **kite**. Show that this kite has two pairs of sides that are equal in length.

   c. Use the slope of the sides to prove that for this kite, side $OA \perp AB$ and side $OC \perp BC$.

   d. Are the two triangles, $\triangle OAB$ and $\triangle OCB$, similar triangles? Why or why not?

   e. In any kite, the diagonals are perpendicular. Show that this statement is true for kite $OABC$.

 For Further Reflection

Why does a horizontal line have a slope of 0 (zero)? Why is there no slope for a line that is vertical?

Reaching All Learners

Intervention

When discussing the slope of a vertical line in the For Further Reflection problem, be sure to explain why division by zero is impossible.

Vocabulary Building

Have students define a kite in their own words. Then have them give examples of various kites using different positions of the two diagonals.

Solutions and Samples

Answers to Check Your Work

1. a. The slope of the perpendicular line is $-\frac{3}{2}$ or $-1\frac{1}{2}$.

b. The slope of a parallel line is $\frac{2}{3}$.

2. a.

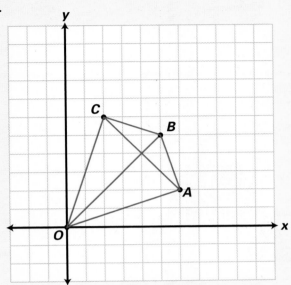

b. The pair *OA* and *OC* have equal lengths and the pair *AB* and *BC* have equal lengths. Sample explanations:

- From *O* to *A*, you go six units to the right and two units up. From *O* to *C*, you go two units to the right and six units up. This covers the same distance for *OA* and *OC*. The same reasoning can be used for *AB* and *BC*.

- Use the Pythagorean theorem to calculate the side lengths, $6^2 + 2^2 = OA^2$ and $2^2 + 6^2 = OC^2$. You do not even have to decide the answers are equal!

  $AB^2 = 3^2 + 1^2$, and so is BC^2.

c. The slope of side *OA* is $\frac{2}{6}$, or $\frac{1}{3}$; the slope of side *AB* is $\frac{-3}{1}$, or -3.

The slopes are opposite and reciprocal numbers. This proves that sides *OA* and *AB* are perpendicular, or side $OA \perp AB$.

The slope of side *OC* is $\frac{6}{2}$, or 3; the slope of side *BC* is $\frac{-1}{3}$, or $-\frac{1}{3}$.

The slopes are opposite and reciprocal numbers. This proves that *OC* and *CB* are perpendicular, or $OC \perp CB$.

d. Yes, $\triangle OAB \sim \triangle OCB$. You could say the multiplication factor is 1 because corresponding side lengths are equal. This also means the triangles are congruent.

Hints and Comments

Overview

Students read the Summary, which reviews the main concepts covered in this section. They use the Check Your Work problems as self-assessment. The answers to these problems are also provided in the Student Book, pages 63 and 64.

Planning

After students complete Section E, you may assign for homework appropriate activities from the Additional Practice section, located on Student Book page 56.

e. The slope of diagonal *OB* is $\frac{5}{5}$, or 1. The slope of diagonal *AC* is $\frac{-4}{4}$, or -1. Since -1 and 1 are each other's opposite and reciprocal numbers, this proves that diagonals *OB* and *AC* are perpendicular.

For Further Reflection

The slope of a line can be found by calculating:

$$\text{slope} = \frac{\text{vertical distance}}{\text{horizontal distance}}$$

If the vertical change for the line is 0 (horizontally flat), then the slope will be 0. If the horizontal change is 0 (that is, a vertical line), then the slope ratio will be some number divided by 0 (undefined on a calculator), or no slope.

Additional Practice

Section Ⓐ Tessellations

1. Here is part of a tessellation for a large triangle.

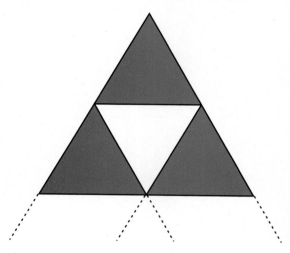

   a. Show how the triangle will look when it has five rows.

   b. If the large triangle has ten rows, how many small triangles will there be altogether?

2. Which triangles are congruent?

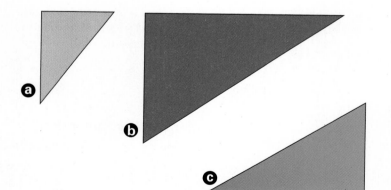

Section A. Tessellations

1. a. When it has five rows, the triangle will look
similar to the triangle shown.

b. There will be 100 small triangles altogether.
Sample strategies:

- Add the number of the triangles in each row:

$$1 + 3 + 5 + 7 + 9 + 11 + 13 + 15 + 17 + 19 = 100$$

- Find a pattern by using a table.

Ten rows will have 10^2, or 100, small triangles.

Row(s)	Total Patches
1	1
2	4
3	9
4	16
5	25
⋮	⋮
x	x^2

2. The triangles labeled **a** and **d** are congruent.

3. In triangle *ABC*, *AB* = 350 cm, *BC* = 275 cm, and *AC* = 300 cm.
You can tessellate △*ABC* with △*DEC*.

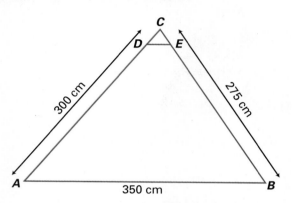

a. If *DE* = 14 cm, what are the lengths of the other sides of
△*DEC*?

b. Find another triangle that you can use to tessellate △*ABC*.

Section Ⓑ Enlargement and Reduction

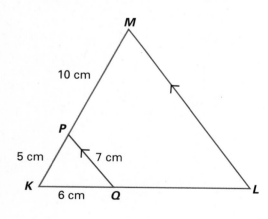

1. In this drawing, there are two triangles;
△*KLM* is an enlargement of △*KQP*.

Angelica says, "*ML* = 14 cm and *QL* = 12 cm
because the multiplication factor is two."

a. How would you explain to Angelica
that her reasoning is wrong?

b. Find the length of side *ML*.

Section A. Tessellations (Continued)

3. a. The side lengths of $\triangle DEC$ are 11, 12, and 14.

Sample explanation:

Along the edge AB, 25 triangles with the shape of $\triangle DEC$ will fit, because

$350 \div 14 = 25.$

This means that along the other edges, there will be also 25 triangles shaped like $\triangle DEC$.

$300 \div 25 = 12$, $DC = 12$

$275 \div 25 = 11$, $CE = 11$

b. A triangle with side lengths of 70 cm, 60 cm, and 55 cm could also be used to tessellate $\triangle ABC$.

Section B. Enlargement and Reduction

1. a. Sample explanation:

Angelica thinks that the multiplication factor is two because segment $KP = 5$ cm and segment $PM = 10$ cm. But segment PM is not the length of a side of a triangle, and you have to look for two similar triangles and compare the sides.

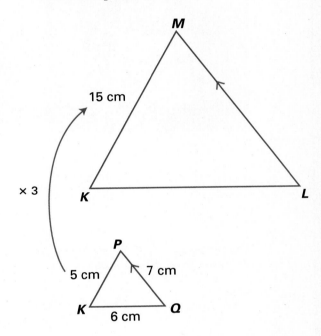

b. The multiplication factor is 3, so side $ML = 21$ cm (7×3).

Additional Practice

Here is a picture taken in Hawaii.
The dimensions are 9 cm × 6.5 cm.

2. a. What enlargement would
you recommend so that this
photo will fit in a frame size,
27 cm × 20 cm, without cutting
it off?

b. Another standard size frame
measures 20 cm × 15 cm.
Deon thinks you can get the
extra 2 cm to each side of the
18 cm × 13 cm photo by using
a multiplication factor of 2.
Is Deon right? Explain.

Section **C** Similarity

1. This diagram shows two overlapping
triangles. Angles with equal measures
are marked with the same symbol.

  a. Explain why these triangles
  are similar.

  b. Find the length of side *PR*.

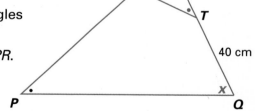

2. Are these triangles similar? Explain.

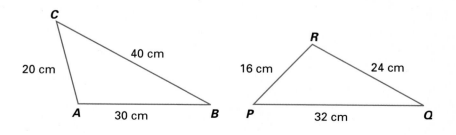

Section B. Enlargement and Reduction (Continued)

2. a. If you use an enlargement factor of 3, the new dimensions are 3 × 6.5 cm = 19.5 cm and 3 × 9 = 27 cm. The enlarged photo fits in the frame without cutting it off; the width is 0.5 cm too small to fit exactly.

b. Deon is not right. Sample explanation:

If you use a multiplication factor of 2, the dimensions will be multiplied by 2; you do not add 2 cm to each dimension.

Section C. Similarity

1. a. Sample explanation:

Each triangle has an angle marked with an × and an angle marked with a dot (angles with the same marks are equal), and both triangles contain angle *R*. Since the three angles of each triangle have equal measures, the triangles are similar.

b. The length of side *PR* is 105 centimeters. Sample strategy:

The side *SR* corresponds to the side *QR*. The multiplication factor is 3.5 (20 × 3.5 = 70). The side *TR* corresponds to the side *PR*. So side *PR* = 30 cm × 3.5 = 105 cm.

2. Yes, $\triangle ABC \sim \triangle RPQ$. Sample strategy:

The following table shows that corresponding sides have the same multiplication factor.

AC = 20 cm	BC = 40 cm	AB = 30 cm
RP = 16 cm	QP = 32 cm	RQ = 24 cm

× 0.8

Section Ⓓ Similar Problems

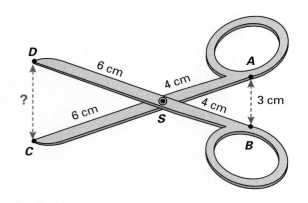

1. Here is a diagram of a pair of scissors. Tommy wants to use the scissors. He opens them so the distance between points *A* and *B* is 3 cm.

   a. What is the distance between the end points *C* and *D*?

   b. His older sister opens the scissors until the distance between *A* and *B* is 5 cm. What is the new distance between the end points *C* and *D*?

Iron-With-Ease Manufacturing wants to make ironing boards that have an adjustable height but maintain a horizontal surface.

The drawing shows a designer's plan for the ironing board. The surface of the board is horizontal.

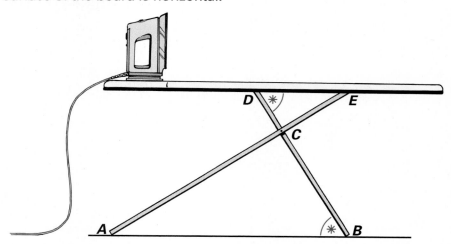

2. a. What must be true about the two angles marked with asterisks (*) as the height of the ironing board changes?

   b. What do you know about other pairs of angles as the height of the ironing board changes?

   c. What do you know about △*ABC* and △*EDC*? Explain.

   d. Suppose the ironing board is in a position so that *AC* = 110 cm, *CE* = 40 cm, and *BC* = 70 cm. Find the length of side *CD*.

Section D. Similar Problems

1. a. The length of *CD* is 4.5 cm. Sample explanation:

In the drawing you see two triangles. These triangles are both isosceles triangles. The vertex angles are equal, so the other angles must also be equal. So the two triangles are similar.

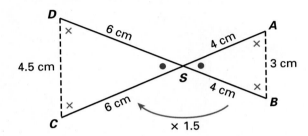

The multiplication factor is 1.5, so the length of *CD* is 3 cm × 1.5 = 4.5 cm.

b. The new length of *CD* is 7.5 cm. The explanation is similar to the one for problem 1a. The multiplication factor is 1.5, so the length of *CD* is 5 cm × 1.5 = 7.5 cm.

2. a. The angles must have equal measures because the board should stay horizontal.

b. Angles *A* and *E* and the two vertical angles at C must be equal.

c. They are similar because all corresponding angles are equal.

d. The length of *CD* is about 25.5 centimeters.

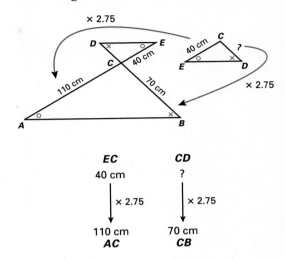

EC	CD
40 cm	?
↓ × 2.75	↓ × 2.75
110 cm	70 cm
AC	**CB**

Sample strategy:

70 ÷ 2.75 ≈ 25 cm

Note: Discuss with students why the answer is rounded to a whole number.

Additional Practice

Section **E** Coordinate Geometry

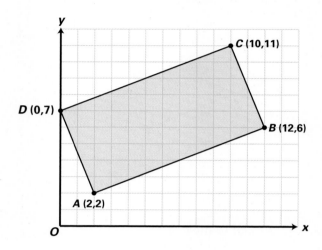

If you want to prove that a quadrilateral is a rectangle, you need to show:

- opposite sides are parallel, and

- adjacent sides are perpendicular.

1. a. Prove that quadrilateral *ABCD* is a rectangle.

   b. In any rectangle, the diagonals have the same length. Show that the diagonals of quadrilateral *ABCD* are equal in length.

2. Find the distance between the two points $P(-7, -5)$ and $Q(3, 8)$ in a coordinate system. Use a calculator and round your answer to one decimal.

Section E. Geometry Coordination

1. a. The straight line through A (2, 2) and B (12, 6) has slope $\frac{6-2}{12-2} = \frac{4}{10}$ or $\frac{2}{5}$.

The straight line through D (0, 7) and C (10, 11) has slope $\frac{11-7}{10-0} = \frac{4}{10}$ or $\frac{2}{5}$.

Lines that have the same slope are parallel, so $AB \parallel DC$.

The straight line through A (2, 2) and D (0, 7) has a negative slope: $\frac{7-2}{0-2} = \frac{5}{-2}$ or $-\frac{5}{2}$.

The straight line through B (12, 6) and C (10, 11) has a negative slope: $\frac{11-6}{10-12} = \frac{5}{-2}$ or $-\frac{5}{2}$.

Lines that have the same slope are parallel, so $AD \parallel BC$.

If you compare the slope of AB, which is $\frac{2}{5}$, and AD, which is $\frac{5}{-2}$, you can see they are opposite and reversed. This means $AB \perp AD$. The same reasoning holds for AB and BC, so $AB \perp BC$.

ABCD is a parallelogram.

b. $AC = BD = 12$. Sample explanations

- Using the Pythagorean theorem:

$8^2 + 9^2 = AC^2$

$64 + 81 = AC^2$

$AC^2 = 145$

$AC = \sqrt{145} \approx 12$

$1^2 + 12^2 = BD^2$

$1 + 144 = BD^2$

$BD^2 = 145$

$BD = \sqrt{145} \approx 12$

- Using congruent triangles

$\triangle ABD$ is congruent to $\triangle ABC$. They fit on top of each other. This means that $AC = BD$.

- Using symmetry

You can use two different folding lines to fold rectangle *ABCD* in two halves that are symmetric. This means $AC = BD$, and these diagonals are cut into halves at their intersection point.

2. $PQ = \sqrt{269} \approx 16.4$. Sample explanation:

$10^2 + 13^2 = PQ^2$

$100 + 169 = PQ^2$

$PQ^2 = 269$

$PQ = \sqrt{269} \approx 16.4$

Assessment Overview

Unit assessments in *Mathematics in Context* include two quizzes and a Unit Test. Quiz 1 is to be used anytime after students have completed Section B. Quiz 2 can be used after students have completed Section D. The Unit Test addresses most of the major goals of the unit. You can evaluate student responses to these assessments to determine what each student knows about the content goals addressed in this unit.

Pacing

Each quiz is designed to take approximately 25 minutes to complete. The Unit Test is designed to be completed during a 45-minute class period. For more information on how to use these assessments, see the Planning Assessment section on the next page.

Goals	Assessment Opportunities		Problem Level
• Identify congruent and similar figures.	Quiz 1 Quiz 2 Test	Problem 3 Problems 2, 3a Problems 1ab	
• Recognize and use patterns in arrangements of congruent triangles.	Quiz 1 Test	Problem 2 Problems 2ab	
• Identify corresponding sides in similar figures.	Quiz 1 Quiz 2 Test	Problems 1, 3 Problem 1a Problems 1abc	Level I
• Find a multiplication factor for similar figures.	Quiz 1 Quiz 2 Test	Problems 1, 2, 3 Problems 1b, 3b Problems 1c, 2a	
• Determine unknown lengths in given similar figures.	Quiz 1 Quiz 2 Test	Problems 1, 3 Problem 1c Problems 1c, 2a	
• Understand the relationship between parallel lines and equal angles.	Quiz 2	Problem 3c	
• Prove that two triangles are similar.	Quiz 1 Quiz 2	Problem 3 Problem 3c	Level II
• Use properties of similar triangles to solve problems.	Quiz 1 Test	Problems 2, 3 Problems 3, 4bd	
• Choose appropriate models and tools to solve geometric problems.	Test	Problem 3	
• Reason about and use the concepts of ratio and similarity in solving problems.	Test	Problem 4c	Level III

About the Mathematics

These assessment activities assess the majority of the goals for *It's All the Same*. Refer to the Goals and Assessment Opportunities section on the previous page for information regarding the goals that are assessed in each problem. Some of the problems that involve multiple skills and processes address more than one unit goal. To assess students' ability to engage in non-routine problem solving (a Level III goal in the Assessment Pyramid), some problems assess students' ability to use their skills and conceptual knowledge in new situations. For example, in the tent cover problem on the Unit Test (problem 3), students must choose an appropriate representation and strategy to solve a realistic problem involving similarity.

Planning Assessment

These assessments are designed for individual assessment; however, some problems can be done in pairs or small groups. It is important that students work individually if you want to evaluate each student's understanding and abilities.

Make sure you allow enough time for students to complete the problems. If students need more than one class session to complete the problems, it is suggested that they finish during the next mathematics class, or you may assign select problems as a take-home activity. Students should be free to solve the problems their own way. It is assumed that students will have access to rulers and compass cards (or protractors) when completing these assessments. Student use of a calculator on these assessments is at the teacher's discretion.

If individual students have difficulties with any particular problems, you may give the student the option of making a second attempt after providing him or her a hint. You may also decide to use one of the optional problems or Extension activities not previously done in class as additional assessments for students who need additional help.

Scoring

Solution and scoring guides are included for each quiz and the Unit Test. The method of scoring depends on the types of questions on each assessment. A holistic scoring approach could also be used to evaluate an entire quiz.

Several problems require students to explain their reasoning or justify their answers. For these questions, the reasoning used by students in solving the problems as well as the correctness of the answers should be considered in your scoring and grading scheme.

Student progress toward goals of the unit should be considered when reviewing student work. Descriptive statements and specific feedback are often more informative to students than a total score or grade. You might choose to record descriptive statements of select aspects of student work as evidence of student progress toward specific goals of the unit that you have identified as essential.

Use additional paper as needed.

1. In the triangle △*ABC*, arrows are used to indicate that
line *DE* ‖ line *AB*.

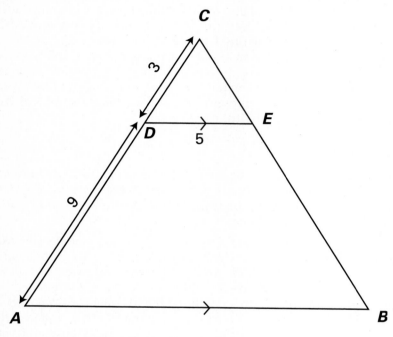

Using the information shown, find the length of *AB*.
Show your work.

2. A small triangle is used to tessellate △*ABC*. Use the given lengths of *CD*, *DE*, and *EB* to find the lengths of the sides of △*ABC*.

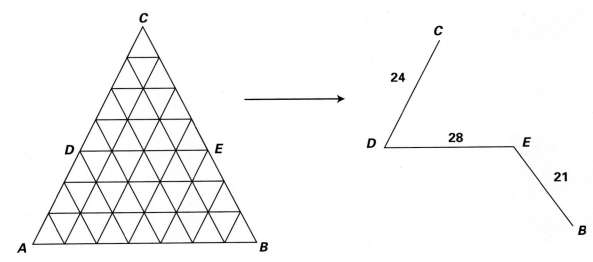

AC =

AB =

CB =

3. Use the information given below to find the lengths of the sides of △*TQS*.

PQ and *AB* are parallel.

RS and *AC* are parallel.

AB = *54* cm

AR = *18* cm

AC = *36* cm

AP = *12* cm

BC = *27* cm

TS =

TQ =

SQ =

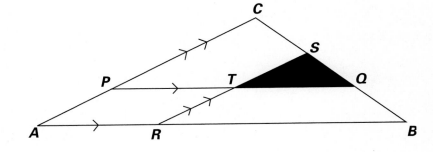

Use additional paper as needed.

1. The two parallelograms *ABCD* and *EFGH* are similar in shape. The lengths of corresponding sides are related by a multiplication factor.

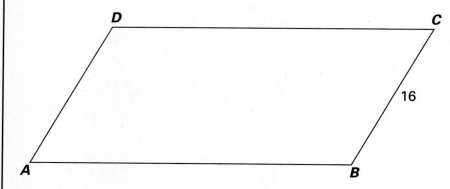

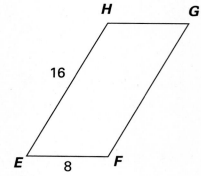

   a. Identify the four pairs of corresponding sides.

   b. What is the multiplication factor for parallelogram *ABCD* and parallelogram *EFGH*?

   c. Find the length of *DC*. Show your work.

2. Are these right triangles similar? Explain why or why not.

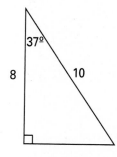

© Encyclopædia Britannica, Inc. This page may be reproduced for classroom use.

Mathematics in Context

3. a. Are these two rectangles similar? Explain why or why not.

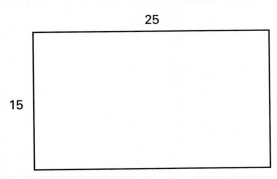

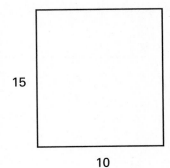

b. The rectangles shown below are similar. Find their multiplication factor.

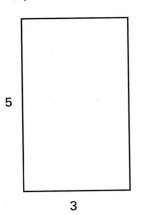

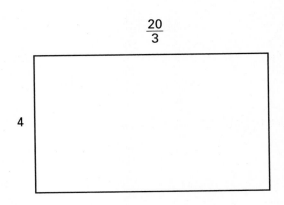

c. Obtuse △PQR is given below. Draw and label another triangle that is similar to △PQR.

Explain how you know your triangle is similar to △PQR.

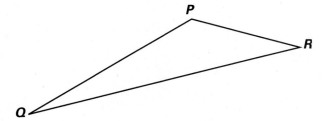

It's All the Same Unit Test

Use additional paper as needed.

1. *ABCD* is a parallelogram. *EF* ‖ *AB*, *AB* = 10 cm, *EF* = 4 cm,
   CF = 2 cm.

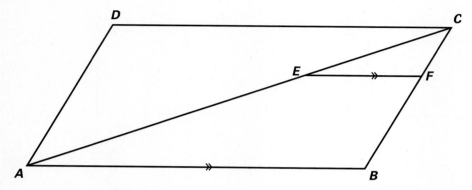

   a. Identify a pair of similar triangles in this figure.

   b. Identify a pair of congruent triangles in this figure.

   c. Find the length of *AD*.

2. In the sequence of figures below, analyze how the fourth figure was constructed from the first one.

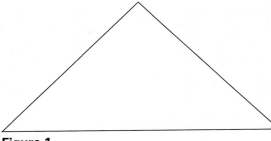

Figure 1

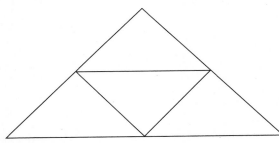

Figure 2

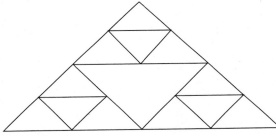

Figure 3

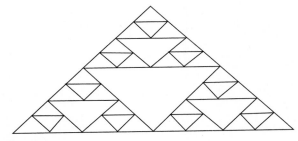

Figure 4

a. Compare the smallest triangle in **Figure 4** to the triangle of **Figure 1**. These triangles are similar. Find the multiplication factor from the small triangle to the triangle in figure 1.

b. How many of the smallest triangles in **Figure 4** could completely tessellate the triangle of **Figure 1**?

Use additional paper as needed.

3. Patricia wants to make a two-sided canvas panel, as shown below by the dotted lines, to protect the two rectangular sides of her camping tent against heavy rain storms. She wants to anchor the bottom of the canvas panel a distance of 0.25 meters away from the actual tent. Patricia also wants to make sure that the canvas panel is parallel to the sides of the tent.

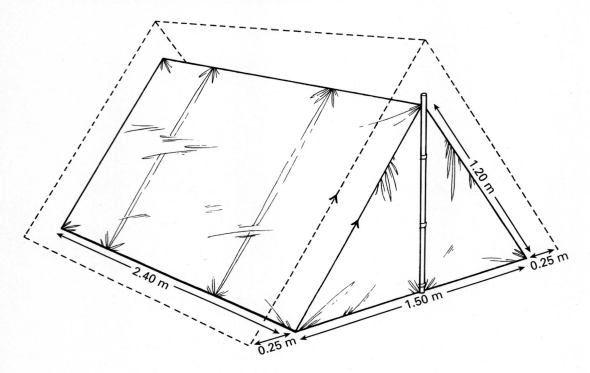

If the canvas material costs $4.95 per square meter, what is the price of the material Patricia needs to make the canvas panel? Explain how you found your answer.

4. a. A straight line has a slope of $\frac{2}{3}$. What is the slope of the line that is perpendicular to this line?

b. In your own coordinate system, use the following information to draw triangle $\triangle OAB$.

Point O is the origin of the coordinate system, $O(0,0)$.

Point A has coordinates $A(3, 2)$.

$\angle A$ is a right angle.

Point B is on the y-axis.

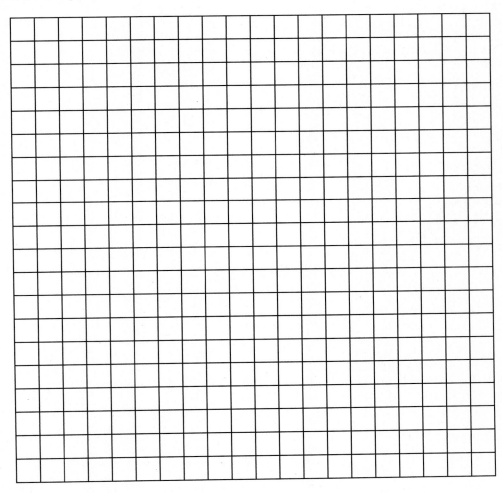

c. Find the exact coordinates of point B. Show your calculations and check them with your drawing of problem 4b.

d. Right triangle $\triangle PAQ$ is similar to $\triangle OAB$. The sides of $\triangle PAQ$ are three times the length of the sides of $\triangle OAB$.
Both triangles share the same vertex $A(3, 2)$. Find the coordinates of points P and Q.

It's All the Same Quiz 1
Solution and Scoring Guide

Possible student answer	Suggested number of score points	Problem level
1. $AB = 20$ Sample student explanation: Four small triangles $\triangle DEC$ can tessellate the large triangle $\triangle ABC$ along each side. The factor of enlargement is 4 since $DC = 3$ and $AC = 12$.	**4** (Award 2 points for a correct answer, 2 points for a correct explanation.)	I
2. $AC = 42$; $AB = 49$; $BC = 49$ Students may use the given lengths of CD, DE, and EB to determine that each small triangle in $\triangle ABC$ has sides of 6, 7, and 7, as shown below. Using the lengths of the small triangle, students can determine the total length of each side. Length of AC, $6 \times 7 = 42$. Lengths of AB and BC, $7 \times 7 = 49$.	**3** (Award 1 point for each correct side length.)	I/II

Possible student answer	Suggested number of score points	Problem level
3. $TS = 12$ cm; $TQ = 18$ cm; $QS = 9$ cm Sample student drawing :	**6** (Award 2 points for each correct side length. Do not subtract score points if students did not add a unit of measurement with their answers.)	**I/II**

Sample student drawing :

(Triangle diagram with labels: C at top, S and 27 to the right of C; P, 18, T below left; 12, A, 18, R, 36, B along the bottom; 24 on segment from A to C; 18 between S and Q; 12 near R; with shaded triangle TSQ)

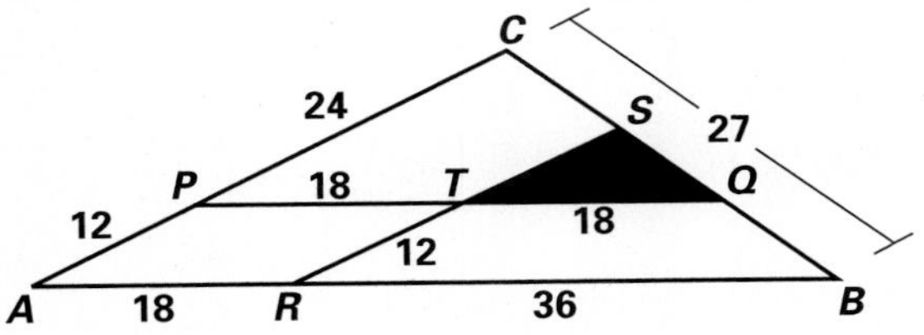

Sample strategy:

Since $AC \parallel RS$ and $AB \parallel PQ$, quadrilateral $ARTP$ is a parallelogram, and $AR = PT$, and $AP = RT$. So $PT = 18$ cm, and $RT = 12$ cm. (Students may have noted this directly in their own drawing.)

Since $\triangle ABC \sim \triangle PQC$, (equal angles), we can use the following ratio table:

$\triangle ABC$	$AB = 54$	$AC = 36$
$\triangle PQC$	$PQ = ?$	$PC = 24$

$\times 1.5$

So $PQ = 36$ cm, and

$TQ = 36$ cm $- 18$ cm $= 18$ cm.

Since $\triangle TQS$ is similar to both $\triangle ABC$ and $\triangle PQC$, we can use two ratio tables to find the length of sides TS and QS.

$\triangle PQC$	$PC = 24$	$PQ = 36$
$\triangle TQS$	$TS = ?$	$TQ = 18$

$\times 2$

$\triangle ABC$	$AB = 54$	$BC = 27$
$\triangle TQS$	$TQ = 18$	$QS = ?$

$\times 3$

Total score points	**13**	

It's All the Same Quiz 2
Solution and Scoring Guide

Possible student answer	Suggested number of score points	Problem level

1. a. Corresponding sides:
    AB and *EH* or *FG*
    DC and *FG* or *EH*
    AD and *EF* or *GH*
    BC and *GH* or *EF*
	4
	(Award 1 point for each correct pair.)
		I

b. The multiplication factor from *EFGH* to *ABCD* is 2.	**1**	I
c. The length of *DC* is 32. Possible explanation: The multiplication factor from *EFGH* to *ABCD* is × 2. The largest side in *EFGH* is 16; 2 × 16 = 32.	**2** (Award 1 point for a correct answer, 1 point for correct work.)	I
2. Yes, the triangles are similar. Possible explanation: The angle measures for both triangles are the same. The angle measures of the large right triangle are 90°, 37°, and 53° since the three measures add up to 180°. The angle measures for the small right triangle are also 90°, 37°, and 53°. So the two triangles must be similar.	**3** (Award 1 point for a correct conclusion, 2 points for a correct explanation that indicates either same angle measures or a multiplication factor of 2.)	I

Possible student answer	Suggested number of score points	Problem level
3. a. The rectangles are <u>not</u> similar Possible explanation: 		Large Rectangle	15	25
Small Rectangle	10	15	 $10 \times 1.5 = 15$, but $15 \times 1.5 \neq 25$. There is no common multiplication factor.	**2** (Award 1 point for a correct answer, 1 point for correct work.)	I
b. The multiplication factor for the rectangles of problem b is $\frac{4}{3}$ or $1\frac{1}{3}$. Since the rectangles are similar, the ratio of the side lengths should be the same for all corresponding sides. 		Large Rectangle	$\frac{20}{3}$	20	4
Small Rectangle	5	15	3		**2**	I
c. See student drawing. All angles for the new figure should be equal to the angles in the first figure.	**2**	II
Total score points	**16**	

It's All the Same Unit Test
Solution and Scoring Guide

Possible student answer	Suggested number of score points	Problem level
1. a. $\triangle EFC \sim \triangle ABC$.	1	I
b. $\triangle ADC$ is congruent to $\triangle CBA$.	1	I
c. $AD = 5$ cm. Possible student work: $\triangle EFC \sim \triangle ABC$ (equal angle measures). AB and EF are corresponding sides. The multiplication factor is $2\frac{1}{2}$ because $2\frac{1}{2} \times 4 = 10$. FC and BC are corresponding sides. $BC = 2\frac{1}{2} \times 2 = 5$ $AD = BC$	3 (Award 1 point for a correct answer, 2 points for a correct explanation.)	I
2. a. The multiplication factor is 8. 8 small triangles fit along each side of the large triangle.	2 (Award 1 point for a correct answer, 1 point for a correct explanation.)	I
b. 64 small triangles could completely tessellate the large triangle.	1	I
3. The cost of the canvas is $38.02. Sample strategy: I made a front-view sketch of the tent and canvas panel. Since the sides of both triangles are parallel to each other, the angles formed by the sides must also be equal. So the triangles formed by the tent and canvas panel are similar triangles. **[diagram of nested triangles: "New Side", "1.20 m", base segments "0.25 m", "1.50 m", "0.25 m", total "2.00 m"]** The base of the large triangle is 2 m, and the base of the small triangle is 1.5 m, so the multiplication factor is $\frac{4}{3}$. ($2 \div 1.5 = \frac{4}{3}$)	5 (Award 1 point for a correct answer, 1 point for indicating the two triangles are similar, 1 point for a correct multiplication factor, 1 point for the correct dimensions of the canvas, and 1 point for a correct calculation of area.)	II/III

Possible student answer	Suggested number of score points	Problem level
One side of the canvas panel is 1.6 m. $(1.2 \times \frac{4}{3} = 1.6)$ The total length of the canvas panel must be 2×1.6 m, or 3.2 m. The width of the canvas panel is the same as the width of the tent, 2.4 meters. Area = 3.2 m × 2.4 m = 7.68 m². To find the total cost of the material, I multiplied the price per square meter, \$4.95, times the total area, 7.68 m² × \$4.95 ≈ \$38.02.		
4. a. The perpendicular line has slope $= -\frac{3}{2}$, or $-1\frac{1}{2}$.	2	I
b. Note that students may use the answer of problem 4a to find point B on the y-axis.	2 (Award 1 point for a correct drawing, 1 point for neatness.)	II
c. $B (0, 6\frac{1}{2})$ Sample response: Since $AB \perp OA$, I could use the slope of $AB = -\frac{3}{2}$. From point A, I made a step of 2 left and 3 up and then a half-step of 1 left and $1\frac{1}{2}$ up. So the y-coordinate of B is $2 + 3 + 1\frac{1}{2} = 6\frac{1}{2}$.	3 (Award 2 points for the correct coordinates of point B, 1 point for a correct explanation.)	III
d. $P(-6, -4)$; $Q(-6, 15\frac{1}{2})$	2	II
Total score points	22	

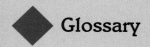

Glossary

The Glossary defines all vocabulary words indicated in the unit. It includes the mathematical terms that may be new to students as well as words having to do with the contexts introduced in the unit. (Note: The Student Book has no Glossary in order to allow students to construct their own definitions based on their personal experiences with the unit activities.)

The definitions below are specific to the use of the terms in this unit. The page numbers given are from this Teacher's Guide.

acute angle (p. 29) an angle smaller than 90°

congruent (p. 2) having the same shape and size

corresponding sides of similar triangles (p. 12) the matching sides of two triangles with the same shape, parallel if the two triangles are placed in the same orientation

corresponding angles of similar triangles (p. 22) the matching angles of two triangles with the same shape, in the same position if the two triangles are placed in the same orientation

diagonal (p. 49) a line segment joining two vertices of a polygon (or polyhedron) with four or more sides (or faces)

distance (p. 49) for two points P and Q in a coordinate system, the length of the line segment PQ

enlarged (p. 10) a figure that is larger in size than an original

equilateral triangle (p. 2T) a triangle with all sides of equal length

family of parallel lines (p. 3) a group of two or more parallel lines (in a plane)

factor of enlargement (p. 9) the number you need to multiply the dimensions of the original object to find the dimensions of the new (enlarged) object

isosceles triangle (p. 2T) a triangle with at least two sides of equal length

kite (p. 51) a quadrilateral formed by two adjacent pairs of equal line segments

line segment AB (p 49) the part (or segment) of the straight line between points A and B

multiplication factor (p. 10) the number by which the dimensions of a shape are multiplied to find a similar shape, enlarged if the multiplication factor is more than 1, reduced if the multiplication factor is smaller than 1, and congruent with the original if the multiplication = 1

obtuse angle (p. 29) an angle greater than 90°

parallel (p. 3) describing lines and planes that do not intersect; they are also always the same distance from each other

perpendicular lines (p. 47) lines that intersect to form right angles (90°)

reduced (p. 10) a figure that is smaller in size than an original

reduction factor (p. 10) the number you need to multiply the dimensions of the original object to find the dimensions of the new (reduced) object

rhombus (p. 2) a quadrilateral with all four sides the same length; rhombuses are always parallelograms

similar triangles (p. 17) triangles that have the same shape, but not necessarily the same size

slope (p. 45) a measure of the steepness and direction of a line; found by using two points on the line; the ratio of the vertical distance between the two points divided by the horizontal distance between the same two points; or the ratio of the components of a direction pair for the line

tessellation (p. 2) an arrangement of polygonal regions covering a shape without overlapping or leaving any gaps

BRITANNICA

Mathematics
in
Context

Blackline
Masters

Dear Family,

Your child will soon begin working in the *Mathematics in Context* unit, *It's All the Same*. Below is a letter to your child, describing the unit and its goals.

In this unit, students explore patterns in arrangements of congruent shapes in tessellations, such as patchwork designs. You can help your child relate the classwork to his or her own life by asking questions such as, *What is a tessellation?* or Do *you see any tessellation patterns here at home, or in our neighborhood?* You might also challenge your child to draw a tessellation for a cookie cutter, tile, or other common household items.

Students also investigate the properties of similar triangles in this unit. You might ask your child to explain the meaning of *similarity* and ask him or her to find some examples of similar shapes or designs in floor tiles or wall paper patterns.

Students use the properties of similar figures to find unknown lengths in similar triangles. You might challenge your child to find the height of a tree or the height of a building using similar triangles.

We hope you enjoy investigating patterns and exploring similarity with your child.

Sincerely,

The Mathematics in Context Development Team

Dear Student,

Did you ever want to know the height of a tree that you could not climb? Do you ever wonder how people estimate the width of a river?

Have you ever investigated designs made with triangles?

In this *Mathematics in Context* unit, *It's All The Same*, you will explore geometric designs called tessellations. You will arrange triangles in different patterns, and you will measure lengths and compare angles in your patterns. You will also explore similar triangles and use them to find distances that you cannot measure directly.

As you work through the problems in this unit, look for tessellations in your home and in your school. Look for situations where you can use tessellations and similar triangles to find lengths, heights, or other distances. Describe these situations in a notebook and share them with your class. Have fun exploring triangles, similarity, and tessellations!

Sincerely,

The Mathematics in Context Development Team

◆ **Student Activity Sheet 2**
Use with *It's All the Same*, page 4.

Name _____

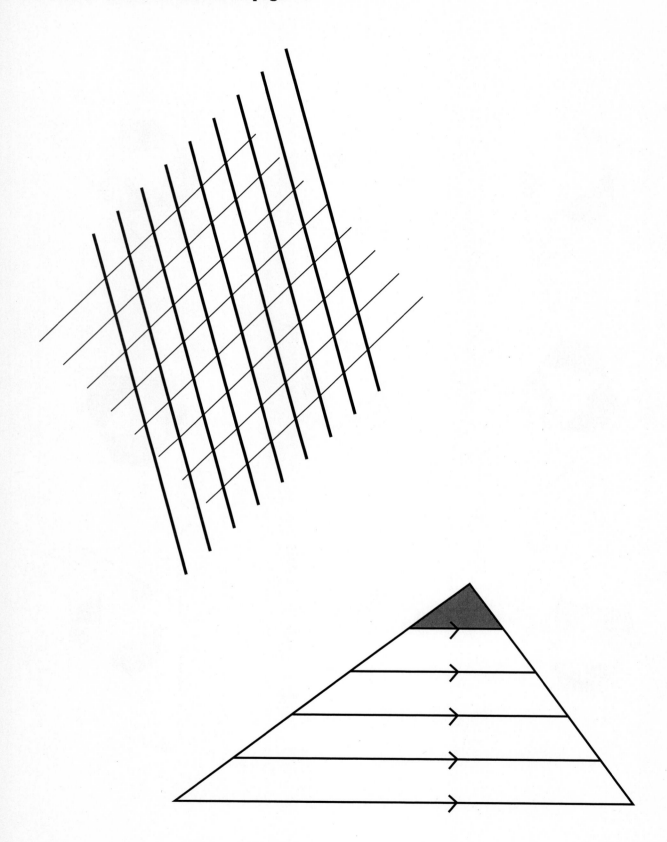

C

B

◆ **Student Activity Sheet 4**
Use with *It's All the Same*, page 31.

Name _____

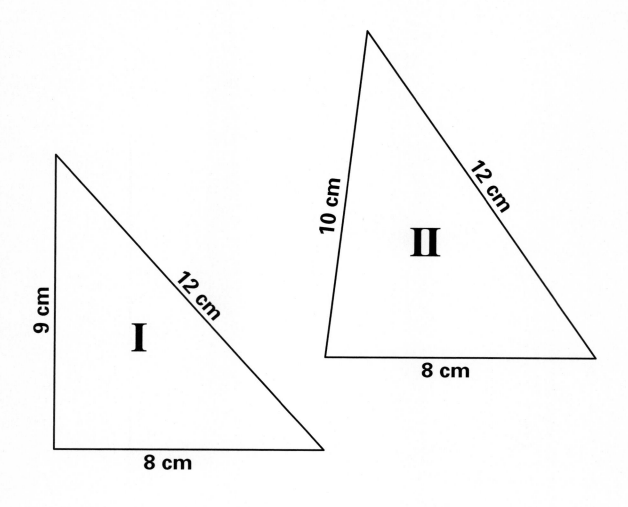

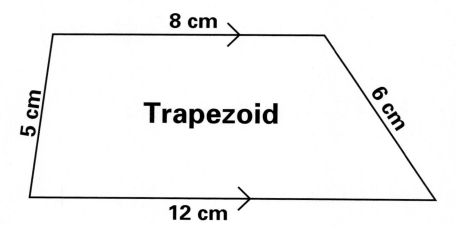

Name _____

Student Activity Sheet 5 ◆
Use with *It's All the Same*, page 38.

Problem 9

◆ **Student Activity Sheet 6**
Use with *It's All the Same*, page 48.

Name _____

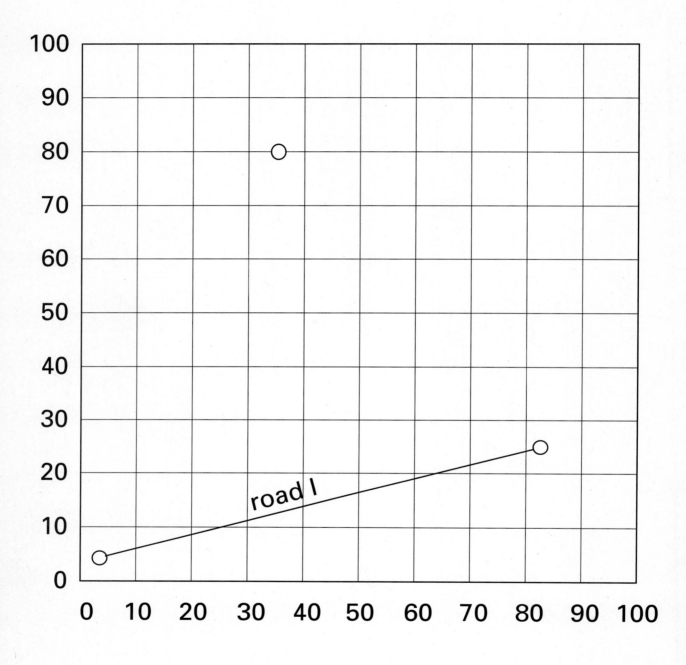